Agriculture in the United Kingdom 2001

Produced by:

Department for Environment, Food and Rural Affairs

Scottish Executive Environment and Rural Affairs Department

Department of Agriculture and Rural Development (Northern Ireland)

National Assembly for Wales Agriculture Department

LONDON: THE STATIONERY OFFICE

Published by The Stationery Office and available from:

The Stationery Office
(mail, telephone, fax & e-mail orders only)
PO Box 29, Norwich, NR3 1GN
Telephone orders/General enquiries: 0870 6005522
Fax orders: 0870 6005533
E-mail: book.orders@tso.co.uk
Textphone 0870 240 3701

You can now order books online at **www.tso.co.uk**

The Stationery Office Bookshops
123 Kingsway, London, WC2B 6PQ
020 7242 6393 Fax 020 7242 6394
68-69 Bull Street, Birmingham B4 6AD
0121 236 9696 Fax 0121 236 9699
9-21 Princess Street, Manchester M60 8AS
0161 834 7201 Fax 0161 833 0634
16 Arthur Street, Belfast BT1 4GD
028 9023 8451 Fax 028 9023 5401
18-19 High Street, Cardiff CF10 1PT
029 2039 5548 Fax 029 2038 4347
71 Lothian Road, Edinburgh EH3 9AZ
0870 606 5566 Fax 0870 6065588

The Stationery Office's Accredited Agents
(see Yellow Pages)

and through good booksellers

First published 2002

ISBN 0 11 243065 1

The paper on which this publication is printed uses pulp from managed forests only and is Total Chlorine Free (TCF)

Printed in the United Kingdom for The Stationery Office

Contents

2001

Statistical tables and charts

List of tables

2001

List of charts

Preface

Legal Basis **1** *Agriculture in the United Kingdom 2001* fulfils the requirement under the Agriculture Act 1993 that Ministers publish an annual report on such matters relating to price support for agricultural produce as they consider relevant and cover in the report developments in agricultural policy, including policy on agriculture and the environment. The Government will draw on this information when considering policy issues, including proposals by the European Commission in respect of the Common Agricultural Policy and the provision of agricultural support in 2001/02

Changes to the Report **2** Some of the figures now given for past years may differ from those published in preceding issues. This is because of the use of later information, changes in the scope and nature of the available data and improvements in statistical methods. Chapter 1 has been reduced in scope and now only reports on the key events of the year in so far as they affect the statistics. The previous wide ranging report on policy developments can be found in the departmental report. Some restructuring of the report has taken place to give more emphasis on subsidies and productivity. The detailed statistics on farm businesses have been removed, but can be found in the sister publication Farm Incomes in the United Kingdom.

Statistical notes **3** Most of the data are on a calendar year basis. The figures for 2001 are provisional; they reflect the position as seen in January 2002 when information for 2001 was still incomplete and an element of forecasting was required.

4 The following points apply throughout:

(a) All figures relate to the United Kingdom, unless otherwise stated.

(b) In the tables
- means 'nil' or 'negligible' (less than half the last digit shown).
..means 'not available' or 'not applicable'.

(c) The figures for imports and exports include those from intervention stocks and the figures for exports include re-exports. Imports are based on country of consignment. Exports are based on country of reported final destination. The source of Overseas Trade Statistics is HM Customs and Excise.

(d) Where statistics are shown for the European Union as a whole they represent the present 15 member states in all years. For example exports of food feed and drink to the EU in 1990 to 1992 includes exports to all 15 member states during that period.

5 This publication and other DEFRA statistics can be found on the internet at www.defra.gov.uk/esg.

Chapter **1** Key events in 2001

2001

Foot and mouth disease

1 The first case of foot and mouth disease was confirmed in a slaughterhouse in Essex on 20 February. It was the most severe outbreak since 1967/8 and affected the life of the country far beyond the farming community and agriculture industry. A total of 2,030 *cases* was confirmed with the disease peaking in March and April. The *areas* most affected formed a broad swathe from south-west Scotland through northern England and eastern Wales to Devon. All counties finally achieved foot and mouth disease free status on 14 January 2002.

2 The total number of *animals slaughtered* was 6.1 million, 4.1 million for disease control purposes and 2.0 million for welfare reasons. Of the total, 4.9 million were sheep. A further 526,000 were slaughtered under the Light Lamb Scheme. Total *compensation* of £1.2 billion was paid to farmers, £1.0 billion in direct payments and £0.2 billion through the Livestock Welfare Disposal Scheme.

3 Throughout the crisis the *export* of livestock and livestock products was banned. Exports of pigmeat from certain foot and mouth disease free counties were resumed at the end of October.

Weather report

4 Autumn 2000 was the wettest for at least 230 years and wet weather continued to be the main feature of the 2000/2001 winter, bringing localised persistent flooding and widespread waterlogging. Much of the land normally sown in the autumn was left unsown for many weeks. Where crops were eventually sown, growth was hindered in the cold, wet soil and crop damage was sometimes severe enough to necessitate re-drilling. In many areas wet conditions also predominated in March and April, hindering fieldwork. Arable farmers elected to enter extra land into set-aside when alternatives looked increasingly unviable.

5 Many autumn sown crops that survived the winter looked poor in the spring and in many areas it was not until well into May that they really restarted. May brought a significant improvement in the weather, enabling catching up of urgent fieldwork. Drier weather continued in June and some crop and grass growth slowed due to lack of moisture.

6 In the main arable areas the harvest progressed smoothly with few serious interruptions. Yields were, however, disappointing – a legacy of the wet autumn, winter and spring. The feature of autumn 2001 was the exceptionally mild weather. Although there were some wet spells, autumn 2001 was much drier overall than the previous autumn and most arable farms completed drilling on time and in good conditions. By the middle of the 2001/2002 winter, most drilling and spraying was up to date, with autumn sown crops looking better than the previous year and the potato and sugar beet harvests virtually complete.

7 Many cattle continued to be housed in spring where the land was too wet to carry them and grass growth insufficient. With livestock housed earlier than usual in the preceding wet autumn, there was inevitable pressure on feed supplies, adding to that caused by livestock retained on farms during the foot and mouth disease outbreak. The mild autumn led to abundant grass growth and many livestock farmers took advantage of these conditions by leaving stock outside for much longer than normal or taking extra cuts of silage. These steps helped ease the pressure on fodder and straw supplies.

8 The value of output (including subsidies directly related to products) was slightly higher, up 0.7 per cent. The volume was 6.0 per cent lower with reduced production of cereals due to wet weather in the winter of 2000/2001 and of livestock due to foot and mouth disease. The prices received by farmers were 7.1 per cent higher due mainly to price rises for milk, potatoes, vegetables, sugar beet, oilseed rape and wheat.

Performance indicators

9 *Total Income From Farming* (TIFF) rose in real terms by 11 per cent to £1.7 billion in 2001 compared with 2000, which is 72 per cent below its peak in 1995. *Gross Value Added* for the industry (which represents agriculture's contribution to national GDP) fell 13 per cent in volume and 1.8 per cent in value. Following a 12 per cent drop in paid labour in 2000 there was a fall of just 2.2 per cent in 2001. *Total factor productivity* decreased by 6.1 per cent. The *Net worth* of the industry benefited by £2.5 billion from income (TIFF) and capital transfers less exceptional losses. Livestock culled due to foot and mouth disease control measures were treated as exceptional losses and the associated compensation treated as capital transfers both of which affect net worth but not income. The underlying details are provided in chapter 6.

10 The relatively high level of sterling has been the dominant factor behind the fall in incomes in recent years. In 2001 the exchange rate was 0.62 pounds per euro, slightly higher than the rate of 0.61 pounds per euro in 2000. When incomes peaked in 1995, however, the exchange rate had been 0.83 pounds per euro.

11 Developments have taken place on how to measure agriculture's impact on the environment. Further work is necessary to establish a framework and then to attach values to items within the framework – see chapter 10.

Subsidies

12 *Direct subsidies*, less levies, paid to the industry rose slightly to £2.5 billion. Spending in the UK under the *CAP* is forecast to increase from £2.9 billion in 2000/2001 to £3.5 billion in 2001/02. The increase is mainly attributable to the impact of the foot and mouth disease outbreak.

13 *Arable Area Payments* totalled £1.0 billion in 2001, which was £50 million less than in 2000. Within this total, *agrimonetary compensation* was £61 million less than in 2000. There was a 21 per cent reduction in the area claimed for wheat and a 53 per cent increase in the area of *set-aside*.

14 Subsidies and other income payments to the *livestock sector* fell by 16 per cent to £1.0 billion. Subsidies to beef producers rose but payments under the *Sheep Annual Premium Scheme* fell due to an increase in the EU average market price. Land area-based schemes replaced the *Hill Livestock Compensatory Allowance* with payments over £50 million higher. Agrimonetary compensation of £67 million was paid to *beef and sheep producers*. *Milk producers* received £79 million in agrimonetary compensation.

15 *Modulation* was introduced at a flat rate of 2.5 per cent in the 2001 scheme year to help fund the Rural Development Programme. On an accruals basis modulation is estimated to reduce arable and livestock subsidies by £44 million in 2001. Payments under *agri-environment schemes* were £64 million higher than in 2000.

2001

Chapter 2 Farming income and agriculture in the economy

Long Term Trends in Farming Income

(Chart 2.1)

1 Total Income From Farming, TIFF, rose slightly in 2001 from a level which was at the lowest point in real terms since the depression in the late 1930s. Although TIFF fluctuates considerably there was a general decline between 1973 and 1990 followed by a sharp rise up to 1995 but then a dramatic fall. Local fluctuations are caused by weather conditions and world commodity prices and, since 1990, shifting exchange rates have been a major factor.

Chart 2.1 UK income trends in real terms at 2001 prices

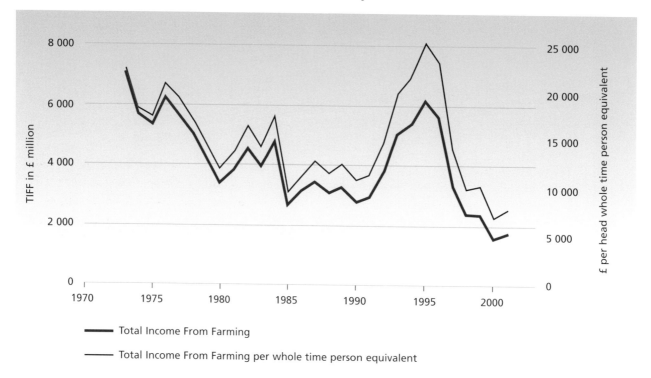

Total Income From Farming

Total Income From Farming per whole time person equivalent

Summary Measures including Total Income from Farming

(Table 2.1)

2 Total Income From Farming in 2001 in the UK is estimated to be £1.7 billion which is 13 per cent (11 per cent in real terms) higher than its 2000 level. TIFF represents business profits plus income to farmers, partners and directors and those with an entrepreneurial interest in the business. In real terms TIFF is forecast to be 72 per cent below its peak in 1995 (after more than doubling between 1990 and 1995). TIFF per annual work unit (AWU) of entrepreneurial labour was 13 per cent higher in real terms at £7,861 in 2001 compared to 2000. Average subsidies per AWU of entrepreneurial labour were higher at £11,293 in real terms, a 2.0 per cent increase on 2000. However, the distribution of subsidies is far from equal with approximately half the farms accounting for 97 per cent of agricultural activity.

3 The overall increase in 2001 masks variation across sectors as they faced differing circumstances and comes despite the impact of foot and mouth disease and a poor cereals harvest. The value of output (including subsidies directly related to products) was slightly higher, up 0.7 per cent. This increase was due to improved prices leading to higher values of output for milk, potatoes and horticulture outweighing lower values of output for cereals and livestock.

4 The *net worth* of the industry benefited from income (TIFF) valued at £1.71 billion and capital transfers worth £1.35 billion. Livestock destroyed due to foot and mouth disease measures are treated as exceptional losses and should count against net worth. This is explained in detail in chapter 6.

5 Cash flow from farming rose in real terms by £1.2 billion or 46 per cent mainly because it includes the compensation for livestock culled as part of the measures taken to eradicate foot and mouth disease. Note that cash flow does not take into account the value of losses of livestock and much of this money will be needed to restock. Cash flow reflects sales rather than production and expenditure on gross fixed capital formation rather than depreciation of capital assets. It includes capital transfers paid to the industry in exchange for assets.

6 Total factor productivity decreased by 6.1 per cent in 2001. The impact of foot and mouth disease reduced productivity in cattle and sheep production. Productivity in the arable sector was also reduced due to poor yields and re-sowing following the wet weather.

Agriculture and food in the national economy

(Table 2.2)

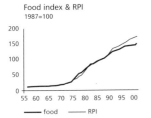

Food index & RPI
1987=100

7 Gross Value Added for the industry, which represents its contribution to national GDP, was down in volume by 13 per cent because of a drop in outputs without a corresponding drop in inputs. However, due to price rises for some outputs, its value was down only by 1.8 per cent. This drop is in part due to the decoupling of some subsidies from products which removes them from output (e.g. the hill livestock compensatory allowance paid per animal has been replaced by the hill farm allowance paid per hectare).

8 The agricultural industry accounted for 0.7 per cent of the total economy in 2001, measured in terms of gross value added. Its share has fallen as prices for agricultural commodities have fallen and brought down gross value added. Its share had been 1.6 per cent in 1995 and almost 3 per cent in 1973.

9 Similarly, the industry's share of the total workforce is falling, now at 2.0 per cent, following a drop of over 20 per cent in the workforce in the last 10 years. As well as people leaving the industry there is a shift from full time to part time work. Following a 12 per cent drop in paid labour in 2000 there was a fall of just 2.2 per cent in 2001. There was also a smaller drop in unpaid labour in 2001, just 1.8 per cent.

10 Imports of food, feed and drink cost £18.4 billion in 2001 - about twice the value of exports which were worth £8.7 billion. The volume of exports fell by 3.6 per cent, cipally due to reductions in exports of meat, cereals and animal feed. After a slight fall in 2000 food prices rose by 3.3 per cent in 2001. All prices, as measured by the retail price index, rose by 1.8 per cent.

11 In 2001 self-sufficiency in food in the United Kingdom fell to its lowest levels since the current series began in 1988. Self-sufficiency in all food was 63 per cent and 75 per cent for indigenous food. This marked decline followed a period of stability from 1997-1999 and a slight fall in 2000. Although the volume of production fell in 2001, prices rose with the result that the value of production was similar to that in 2000. The value of food imports rose while exports continued to decline, partly due to the ban on livestock and livestock products due to foot and mouth disease. Self-sufficiency is calculated as the value of UK production of raw food divided by the value of raw food consumed in the UK.

Geographic Comparisons
(Table 2.3 and chart 2.2)

12 Table 2.3 shows how the UK agricultural industry divides between England, Northern Ireland, Scotland and Wales. Agriculture's share of total economy gross value added is generally declining. It is lowest in England at 0.6 per cent and highest in Northern Ireland at 2.9 per cent. Agriculture's share of regional employment is highest i Norhern Ireland at about 1 in 12 whereas in England it is less than 1 in 60.

13 Chart 2.2 shows estimated changes in income from agricultural activity across the Member States of the European Union, as measured by Eurostat's indicator A. It is based on Net Value Added at factor cost (deflated by the GDP price index) per annual work unit. Provisional figures show a rise in incomes from agricultural activity for EU-15 with all but two of the 15 Member States recording an increase. The EU-15 increase was due to a rise in agricultural income and a continued reduction in the volume of labour.

Net farm incomes by farm type
(Table 2.4)

14 Information on incomes, assets and liabilities of full time businesses in the United Kingdom is provided by the annual Farm Business Surveys, conducted by universities and agricultural colleges in England and Wales, the Department of Agriculture and Rural Development in Northern Ireland, and the Farm Accounts Scheme in Scotland carried out by the Scottish Agricultural College. Summary results of these sample surveys (weighted according to the distribution of holdings by region, farm type, size and tenure recorded in the June 2000 census) are presented and described in this section, together with provisional estimates of net farm income for 2001/02.

15 *Net farm income* is constructed so that the profitability and performance of different types of farms can be compared. It is defined as the return to the principal farmer and spouse for their manual and managerial labour and on the tenant-type capital of the business. Tenant-type assets, which for this purpose are all assumed to be owned by the occupier, include crops, machinery and livestock. Net farm income treats all farms on a consistent basis by assuming that all farms are tenanted. Thus the profitability of farms of different tenure can be compared. For owner-occupied land an imputed rent is included as a cost. In addition, an imputed labour cost is deducted for unpaid family labour (other than the farmer and spouse).

16 *Total Income From Farming* (TIFF) represents business profits plus income to farmers, partners and directors and those with an entrepreneurial interest in the business and is constructed in accordance with internationally agreed national accounting principles. TIFF and its underlying estimates of outputs and inputs feed into the national accounts and ultimately the national estimate for Gross Domestic Product.

TIFF - Aggregate Measure	NET FARM INCOME - Farm Level Measure
Gross output at basic prices	Receipts 3from sales of output plus subsidies
plus	*plus*
Other subsidies less taxes	Crop and livestock valuation change
less	*less*
Total intermediate consumption, rent, paid labour	Expenditure (costs, overheads, fuel, repairs, rent, paid labour)
Total consumption of fixed capital (depreciation)	Depreciation
Interest	Imputed value of unpaid labour
equals	Imputed rent for owner occupiers
Total Income From Farming	*equals*
	Net farm income

17 In addition to the conceptual differences, net farm income figures are for an accounting period that runs from March to February on average, cover full-time farms only and exclude horticulture. Also, the net farm incomes estimate for 2001/2002 excludes farms which were subject to the compulsory culling of livestock for foot and mouth control purposes, whereas these farms are included in TIFF.

18 As can be seen from their respective definitions, net farm income is a narrower income measure than TIFF. As a consequence the annual percentage change in net farm income is more volatile, especially at relatively low levels of income.

19 Movements in *net farm income* over the last decade for each country and for the major farm types (excluding horticulture) are shown by the index numbers presented in Table 2.4. This income measure is a long standing indicator of the economic performance of farm businesses and, to achieve comparability among farms of different types of tenure, it is based on the assumption that all land is tenanted. It represents the return to the farmer and spouse for their manual and managerial labour and on the tenant-type capital of the business such as permanent crops, livestock and machinery (but not land or buildings).

20 Overall, net farm incomes rose by 25% between 1999/00 and 2000/01. Livestock farm types tended to show increases in income and cereal farms showed declines. Incomes on general cropping farms rose.

21 Pig and poultry farms recorded the biggest proportional increase in net farm income, mainly driven by higher pig prices, whilst cereal farms recorded the steepest fall in net farm income. This was a reflection of lower cereal prices from the 2000 harvest compared to the previous year.

22 Provisional estimates of net farm income for 2001/02 are also shown as indices in Table 2.4. These are based on data from 2000/01 accounts projected forward to 2001/02 on the basis of information on prices in 2001/02, subsidy payments, animal populations and marketings, and crop areas and yields. The estimates should be regarded only as broad indicators of the overall effects on income of expected changes in output values and input costs. Incomes on farms subject to compulsory culling of livestock for foot and mouth disease control purposes are not included in these figures.

23 In 2001/02 net farm incomes are forecast to increase by 32% overall in the UK. This is mainly a reflection of a marked increase in incomes on dairy farms. Incomes on dairy farms are forecast to increase by 96%. This is due to higher milk prices in 2001/02 compared to 2000/01. Incomes on general cropping farms and lowland cattle and sheep farms are expected to remain broadly unchanged. Incomes on LFA cattle and sheep farms are expected to decline, mainly due to falls in receipts from Sheep Annual Premium, lower prices for finished lambs and increases in input costs, particularly feed. The expected decline in income on pig and poultry farms is driven by lower pig prices and some contraction in the size of the pig enterprise. The expected fall in income on cereal farms is mainly a reflection of a fall in cereal production volume from the 2001 harvest, and some switching from wheat to less profitable alternative crops following the very wet weather and poor growing conditions that occurred between autumn 2000 and spring 2001.

Prospects for Farming Incomes

24 Forecasts of the industry's future prospects are highly uncertain for two main reasons. Underlying trends are shaped by exchange rates and world commodity prices which are themselves highly uncertain to forecast. Second, ad hoc events (such as weather conditions or disease outbreaks) can push incomes above or below underlying trends in individual years.

25 There are four factors in particular, which will shape future trends over the medium term:

- future market developments;
- the impact of CAP reform;
- future exchange rates;
- performance improvement and industry re-structuring.

26 Initially, forecasts show a continuing recovery, following the increase in incomes in 2001 as production levels return to normal. Thereafter, medium term recovery in world commodity prices will be partly offset by implementation of the Agenda 2000 CAP reforms. The value of production is expected to rise, but so will feed prices and other costs. Consequently, incomes are not expected to recover significantly.

27 The sterling equivalent of direct subsidies, and also the market prices for many commodities, are dependent on the pound/euro exchange rate. The relatively high level of sterling has been the dominant factor behind the fall in incomes in recent years. In 2001 the exchange rate was 0.62 pounds per euro, slightly higher than the rate of 0.61 pounds per euro in 2000. However, when incomes peaked in 1995, the exchange rate had been 0.83 pounds per euro. Sterling is forecast to weaken against the euro over the medium term and this will boost farm incomes, but there is a lot of uncertainty on when, and by how much.

Chart 2.2 Changes in income across the European Union (provisional figures)

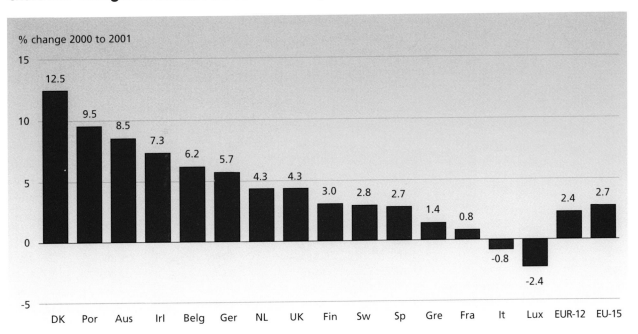

The change in income from agricultural activity as measured by Eurostat, Indicator A, which is based on net value added per whole time person equivalent.

Source: Eurostat - Statistics: Statistics in focus. December 2001

28 The financial pressures of the last few years have resulted in a rapid acceleration in historic rates of productivity growth, including increased labour productivity. It is possible that productivity growth could continue at an even higher rate given the very low level of farm incomes and the impact of recovery from the foot and mouth disease epidemic.

TABLE 2.1 Summary measures from the aggregate agricultural account

Enquiries: Jim Holding on 01904 455080   email: jim.holding@defra.gsi.gov.uk

Calendar years

Year	Net value added at factor cost	Income from farming				Cash flow from farming
		Total income from farming	Compensation of employees	Income from agriculture of total labour input	Total income from farming per AWU of entrepreneurial labour (a)	
£ million		A	B	A + B	(£)	
1990	4 898	2 024	1 715	3 739	7 917	2 314
1991	5 024	2 247	1 779	4 026	8 841	2 763
1992	5 663	2 989	1 784	4 773	11 812	3 131
1993	6 596	4 107	1 787	5 894	16 279	4 077
1994	7 006	4 460	1 827	6 288	17 972	4 349
1995	7 917	5 318	1 836	7 154	21 786	5 071
1996	7 578	4 915	1 881	6 796	20 390	4 811
1997	5 823	3 016	1 930	4 946	12 603	3 141
1998	5 120	2 212	1 977	4 189	9 354	2 860
1999	5 114	2 252	2 028	4 280	9 838	3 027
2000	4 275	1 513	1 897	3 410	6 829	2 536
2001 (provisional)	4 433	1 710	1 914	3 624	7 861	3 757
In real terms, 2001 prices, £ million					(£)	
1990	6 726	2 779	2 356	5 135	10 873	3 177
1991	6 517	2 915	2 308	5 224	11 470	3 585
1992	7 082	3 739	2 231	5 969	14 773	3 916
1993	8 123	5 058	2 200	7 258	20 047	5 021
1994	8 418	5 360	2 196	7 556	21 597	5 226
1995	9 200	6 180	2 134	8 314	25 316	5 892
1996	8 596	5 575	2 133	7 709	23 128	5 457
1997	6 404	3 317	2 122	5 439	13 861	3 455
1998	5 445	2 352	2 102	4 455	9 948	3 041
1999	5 355	2 358	2 124	4 482	10 302	3 170
2000	4 349	1 540	1 930	3 470	6 948	2 580
2001 (provisional)	4 433	1 710	1 914	3 624	7 861	3 757

source: DEFRA Statistics website, www.defra.gov.uk/esg

(a) An annual work unit (AWU) represents the equivalent of an
average full time person engaged in agriculture.

TABLE 2.2 Agriculture and food in the national economy

Enquires: Jim Holding on 01904 455080   email: jim.holding@defra.gsi.gov.uk

Calendar years

	Average of 1990-1992	1997	1998	1999	2000	2001 (provisional)
Agriculture's contribution to total economy gross value added (a)						
at current prices (£ million)	7 522	8 395	7 576	7 317	6 535	6 418
volume index (1995=100)	106.2	100.9	103.4	106.9	104.4	90.7
% of total GVA (current prices)	1.4	1.2	1.0	0.9	0.8	0.7
Workforce in agriculture ('000 persons) (b) (c)	645	611	608	586	557	550
% of total workforce in employment	2.4	2.2	2.2	2.1	2.2	2.2
Gross fixed capital formation in agriculture						
total GFCF at current prices (£ million)	1 972	2 523	2 032	1 639	1 562	1 771
% of national GFCF (current prices)	1.9	1.9	1.4	1.1	1.0	1.1
volume indices (1995=100):						
buildings & works, plant & machinery, vehicles	75.1	84.9	67.0	56.9	53.2	48.0
livestock	93.9	104.6	103.2	96.3	84.8	105.5
Imports of food, feed and drink (£ million) (d) (e)	12 656	17 170	17 198	17 385	17 018	18 399
Imports from the EU:	8 406	10 959	10 979	11 164	10 910	11 694
of which: food, feed and non alcoholic drinks	7 154	9 271	9 198	9 341	9 327	10 116
alcoholic drinks	1 251	1 689	1 781	1 823	1 584	1 578
Imports from the rest of the world:	4 250	6 211	6 220	6 221	6 107	6 706
of which: food, feed and non alcoholic drinks	4 068	5 638	5 565	5 464	5 267	5 722
alcoholic drinks	182	573	655	757	841	984
Volume index (1995=100) (f)	90.4	110.1	119.4	128.6	128.0	135.6
% of total UK imports	10.2	9.1	9.0	8.8	7.6	7.9
Exports of food, feed and drink (£ million) (d) (e)	6 900	9 924	9 246	8 948	8 737	8 612
Exports to the EU:	4 381	5 933	5 865	5 709	5 348	5 197
of which: food, feed and non alcoholic drinks	3 479	4 784	4 738	4 505	4 152	3 965
alcoholic drinks	902	1 149	1 128	1 204	1 196	1 232
Exports to the rest of the world:	2 519	3 991	3 381	3 239	3 389	3 415
of which: food, feed and non alcoholic drinks	1 205	1 978	1 745	1 582	1 645	1 505
alcoholic drinks	1 314	2 012	1 636	1 656	1 744	1 911
Volume index (1995=100) (f)	78.8	103.8	101.2	102.5	101.9	98.2
% of total UK exports	6.5	5.8	5.6	5.4	4.7	4.4
UK self-sufficiency in food as a % of:						
all food	74.4	68.4	67.8	67.9	66.5	62.7
indigenous type food	85.7	81.8	82.0	81.8	80.0	74.9
Household final consumption expenditure on household						
food and alcoholic drinks at current prices (£ million)(g)	67 250	84 175	86 971	90 571	92 758	98 500
of which: household food	44 181	53 832	55 192	56 886	58 252	61 200
alcoholic drinks	23 068	30 343	31 779	33 685	34 506	37 300
at constant 1995 prices (£ million)	75 481	80 896	81 702	83 657	85 657	87 700
of which: household food	47 892	52 347	52 983	54 334	56 123	56 700
alcoholic drinks	27 589	28 549	28 719	29 323	29 534	31 100
% of total household final consumption expenditure	18.7	16.7	16.2	16.0	15.6	15.7
of which: household food	12.3	10.7	10.3	10.0	9.8	9.7
alcoholic drinks	6.4	6.0	5.9	5.9	5.8	5.9
Retail price indices (1995=100)						
food	90.8	103.4	104.7	105.0	104.7	108.2
alcoholic drinks	83.3	105.8	109.4	112.2	113.9	116.3
all items	89.0	105.7	109.3	111.0	114.2	116.3

source: DEFRA Statistics website, www.defra.gov.uk/esg

TABLE 2.2 *cont.*

(a) Agriculture is here defined as in the national accounts, that is net of gross rent and the produce of gardens and allotments.

(b) This series now includes spouses of farmers, partners and directors for the first time. These were excluded in previous editions because consistent data were not available. The effect is to increase the % of total workforce in employment from 2.0% (old basis) in 1997 to 2.3% (new basis) and similarly for previous years.

(c) From 1998 onwards figures are on a different basis to previous years (see headnote to table 3.5).

(d) This aggregate covers SITC divisions 01-09, 11, 22 and section 4.

(e) The figures for 1993 onwards are based on INTRASTAT data and include estimates of non-response and of traders below the threshold for which detailed trade data are not collected.

(f) Data provided by ONS.

(g) 'Household final consumption expenditure' replaced 'Consumer's expenditure' in 1998 when National Accounts adopted the European System of Accounts.

Table 2.3 Summary measures by country in 2001

Enquiries: Jim Holding on 01904 455080   email: jim.holding@defra.gsi.gov.uk

	Gross output (a)	Intermediate consumption	Gross value added at basic prices	Total Income from Farming	Agriculture's share of total regional gross value added at basic prices (b)	Agriculture's share of total regional employment (c)(d)
	£ million	£ million	£ million	£ million	%	%
United Kingdom	15 126	8 707	6 418	1 710	0.7	1.9
England	11 132	6 376	4 757	1 206	0.6	1.5
Wales	967	655	312	47	0.9	4.6
Scotland	1 837	1 013	824	273	1.1	2.9
Northern Ireland	1 189	664	526	190	2.9	7.6

source: DEFRA Statistics website, www.defra.gov.uk/esg

(a) Imported livestock, including purchases of store cattle and sheep, are included as negative output.

(b) In order to estimate the total GVA at basic prices for the entire economy, the fourth quarter has been estimated using the trend of the previous three quarters. This has been apportioned to the countries using the 1998 proportions to give an estimated country GVA at basic prices.

(c) The total workforce in employment consists of employees in employment, the self-employed and work related government training schemes. For Northern Ireland, agriculture's percentage share is higher than that published by the Northern Ireland Department of Enterprise, Trade and Investment, which excludes part-time owners, partners and directors and spouses of farmers from persons engaged in agriculture.

(d) The agriculture industry includes a high proportion of part-time workers. A comparison on the basis of full-time equivalents would show lower percentages.

(e) Due to updated Northern Ireland subsidy data, the country figures for Total Income for Farming do not add up to the UK total.

Table 2.4 Net Farm Income by Country and Type of Farm

Contact: Joe Finlay 020 7270 8623   email: joe.finlay@defra.gsi.gov.uk
Average net farm income per farm: Indices, 1994/95 - 1996/97 = 100   *Accounting years ending on average in February*

	1993/94	1994/95	1995/96	1996/97	1997/98	1998/99	1999/00	2000/01	2001/02 (provisional)
At current prices									
England									
Dairy	115	98	111	91	59	37	24	29	66
Cattle and sheep (LFA)	100	82	108	109	68	36	29	35	31
Cattle and sheep (lowland)	131	101	105	93	11	4	-2	3	4
Cereals	57	76	119	105	40	21	32	17	12
General cropping	64	104	128	68	33	52	13	23	18
Pigs and poultry	28	59	126	114	38	-30	-10	45	26
Mixed	64	82	124	95	21	4	22	20	15
Wales									
Dairy	108	70	122	108	78	43	43	38	60
Cattle and sheep (LFA)	98	49	141	110	67	32	22	28	25
Cattle and sheep (lowland)	89	67	135	98	25	-18	-9	9	-19
Scotland									
Dairy	104	93	111	96	42	14	4	67	154
Cattle and sheep (LFA)	102	84	96	121	52	31	18	43	28
Cereals	42	68	117	116	2	. .	2		2
General cropping	43	131	118	52	-	49	10	203	624
Mixed	102	88	116	97	-14	7	20	25	31
Northern Ireland									
Dairy	89	92	127	82	47	34	33	59	70
Cattle and sheep (LFA)	113	88	105	107	55	5	-3	1	5
United Kingdom									
Dairy	111	93	114	92	59	36	26	35	68
Cattle and sheep (LFA)	102	73	114	113	61	29	18	34	31
Cattle and sheep (lowland)	132	100	109	90	8	-3	-	-	-1
Cereals	56	75	119	106	36	18	29	15	12
General cropping	61	108	126	65	29	50	11	24	24
Mixed	70	84	123	94	15	3	62	61	51
All Types (excluding horticulture)	81	89	119	93	41	27	20	25	33
In real terms (as deflated by the RPI)									
United Kingdom									
Dairy	117	96	114	90	56	32	24	30	59
Cattle and sheep (LFA)	108	76	113	110	57	27	16	30	27
Cattle and sheep (lowland)	140	104	109	88	8	-3	-	-	-
Cereals	59	78	119	103	34	17	26	13	10
General cropping	65	111	126	64	27	46	10	21	21
Pigs and poultry	31	61	126	111	37	-36	-9	41	23
Mixed	74	86	122	91	14	3	56	53	44
All Types (excluding horticulture)	86	91	118	90	38	25	18	22	28

source: DEFRA Statistics website, www.defra.gov.uk/esg

Chapter **3** The structure of the industry

Introduction **1** The tables in this chapter show the size and structure of the UK agricultural industry in 2001 and earlier years. Together they provide information on land use and livestock numbers in UK agriculture, the distribution of these between holdings, the industry's labour force and fixed capital.

Chart 3.1 Agricultural land use

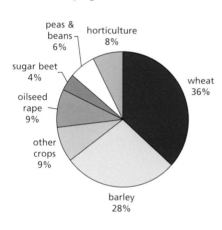

Total area on agriculture holdings

all other land 11%
set-aside 4%
grassland under 5 years 6%
grassland over 5 years 31%
sole right rough grazing 24%
crops 24%

Area of crops grown

peas & beans 6%
horticulture 8%
sugar beet 4%
oilseed rape 9%
other crops 9%
wheat 36%
barley 28%

2 At June 2001 the total area of agricultural land was 18.5 million hectares, some 77 per cent of the total land area in the UK. The June 2001 Census showed a decrease of 4.5 per cent in the area of crops in the UK. The area of cereals decreased by 10 per cent following a 6.6 per cent increase the preceding year. The area of wheat decreased by 22 per cent in 2001 compared with the preceding year, while the area of barley increased by 10 per cent.

3 Numbers of livestock, particularly cattle and sheep, were significantly affected by the outbreak of foot and mouth disease in 2001. Between June 2000 and June 2001 the total cattle population declined by 4.8 per cent. The dairy herd decreased by 3.6 per cent while the beef breeding herd fell by 7.3 per cent. The reduction in beef and dairy cow numbers resulting from the outbreak of foot and mouth disease was offset to some extent by the number of cows retained on farm because of movement restrictions and the temporary closure of the Over Thirty Month Scheme (OTMS).

4 The total number of sheep and lambs fell by 13 per cent between June 2000 and June 2001. The breeding flock fell by 12 per cent, due primarily to the effects of the outbreak of foot and mouth disease but also continuing the decline since 1999.

5 The total number of pigs fell by 9.8 per cent between June 2000 and June 2001. The pig breeding herd - sows in pig, other sows for breeding and gilts in pig – fell by

2.0 per cent. This was primarily due to the contraction of the breeding herd between 1997 and the end of 2000 and the effects of the outbreak of foot and mouth disease in 2001 and the outbreak of Classical Swine Fever in the autumn of 2000.

6 Changes in crop areas between 2000 and 2001 are shown in chart 3.2 and livestock numbers in chart 3.3.

Sizes of holdings and enterprises
(Tables 3.3 and 3.4)

7 Tables 3.3 and 3.4 compare numbers and sizes of holdings and enterprises for 2000 (the latest year available) with five years previously. Data for 1996 and 2001 will be published on the DEFRA website as soon as possible.

8 European size units (ESUs) measure the financial potential of the holding in terms of the margins which might be expected from crops and stock. The margins used are gross margins standardised at average 1987-89 values. The threshold of 8 ESU is judged to be the minimum for full-time holdings. The tables confirm that the trend for larger holdings and enterprises has been maintained.

Labour force in agriculture
(Table 3.5)

9 Following the June Census 2000, an exercise to improve the register of agricultural holdings was undertaken in England. The June 2001 labour figures now include estimates for English holdings that have been converted from the temporary register. Further improvements have also been made to the register in the past year, mainly as a result of livestock tracing. Two sets of results have been produced for June 2001 including and excluding the effects of the exercise. June 2001 (a) is directly comparable with June 2000 and shows a decrease in the total labour force of 1.3 per cent. June 2001(b) reflects the true level of total labour following register improvements.

Fixed capital stock
(Table 3.6)

10 Table 3.6 provides information on the volume of gross stock of fixed capital (excluding land and livestock) available to the agricultural industry. The figures are shown before allowing for depreciation and give a broad indication of how this aspect of the industry's productive capacity has changed over the years. Agriculture's total volume of fixed capital stock is estimated to have been 2.5 per cent lower at the end of 2001 compared to the end of 2000. This is a decline of around 9 per cent on the 1990-92 average level. Over the last few years, all three asset categories *have shown a reduction in fixed capital stock*.

Chart 3.2 Changes in crop area

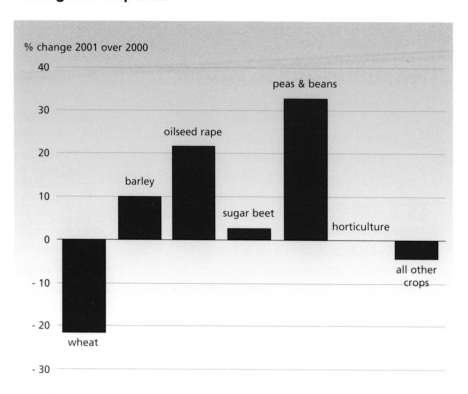

Chart 3.3 Changes in livestock numbers

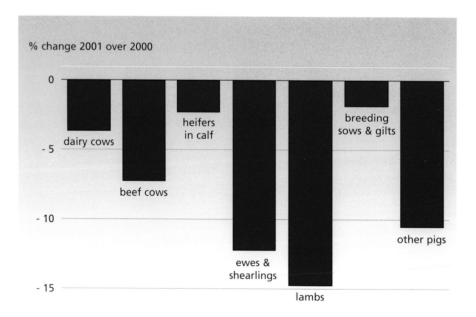

TABLE 3.1 Agricultural land use

Enquiries: Miles Templeton 01904 455306   email: miles.h.templeton@defra.gsi.gov.uk
The data in this table cover all holdings (including minor holdings) in all four countries of the UK. (a)

Thousand hectares   *At June of each year*

	Average of 1990-92	1997	1998	1999	2000	2001
Total agricultural area (total area on agricultural holdings plus common rough grazing)	18 862	18 653	18 604	18 579	18 308	18 549
This comprises:						
Crops	4 984	4 990	4 971	4 709	4 665	4 454
Bare fallow	63	29	34	33	37	43
Total tillage	5 047	5 020	5 005	4 742	4 702	4 497
All grass under five years old	1 599	1 405	1 301	1 226	1 226	1 205
Total arable land	6 646	6 425	6 306	5 968	5 928	5 702
All grass five years old and over (excluding rough grazing)	5 307	5 282	5 364	5 449	5 363	5 584
Total tillage and grass (b)	11 954	11 706	11 671	11 417	11 291	11 286
Sole right rough grazing	4 953	4 657	4 621	4 575	4 445	4 435
Set-aside	110	306	313	572	567	800
All other land (c) and woodland	613	763	773	789	780	801
Total area on agricultural holdings	17 629	17 432	17 377	17 352	17 083	17 323
Common rough grazing (estimated)	1 233	1 221	1 227	1 227	1 226	1 226

source: DEFRA Statistics

(a) From 2000 Scottish minor holdings have been included; data for earlier years are therefore not directly comparable. Also, from 1997 the Northern Ireland census was based on an improved register of holdings and included all active farms having one or more hectares of farmed land plus any below that size which had significant agricultural output. Figures for years before 1997 were revised to be comparable with later years.

(b) Includes bare fallow.

(c) In Great Britain other land comprises farm roads, yards, buildings (excluding glasshouses), ponds and derelict land.

TABLE 3.2 Crop areas and livestock numbers

Enquiries: Miles Templeton 01904 455306   email: miles.h.templeton@defra.gsi.gov.uk

The data in this table cover all holdings (including minor holdings) in all four countries of the UK. (a) (b)

At June of each year

		Average of 1990-92	1997	1998	1999	2000	2001
Crop areas	('000 hectares)						
Total		4 984	4 990	4 971	4 709	4 665	4 454
This comprises:							
Total cereals		3 550	3 514	3 418	3 141	3 348	3 014
of which:	wheat	2 020	2 036	2 045	1 847	2 086	1 635
	barley	1 404	1 359	1 253	1 179	1 128	1 245
	oats	104	100	98	92	109	112
	rye and mixed corn	12	12	11	10	10	7
	triticale	10	8	11	13	16	14
Other arable crops (excluding potatoes)		1 053	1 126	1 209	1 211	979	1 103
of which:	oilseed rape	417	445	507	417	332	404
	sugar beet not for stockfeeding	196	196	189	183	173	177
	hops	4	3	3	3	2	1
	peas for harvesting dry and field beans	209	197	213	202	208	276
	linseed (c)	90	73	100	209	71	31
	other crops	138	211	199	197	192	214
Potatoes		178	166	164	178	166	165
Horticulture		203	184	180	179	172	173
of which:	vegetables grown in the open	139	126	125	126	119	120
	orchard fruit (d)	34	30	30	28	28	28
	soft fruit (e)	15	11	10	9	10	9
	ornamentals (f)	14	14	14	13	14	14
	glasshouse crops	2	2	2	2	2	2
Livestock numbers	('000 head)						
Total cattle and calves		12 040	11 637	11 519	11 423	11 135	10 602
of which:	dairy cows	2 767	2 478	2 439	2 440	2 336	2 251
	beef cows	1 688	1 862	1 947	1 924	1 842	1 708
	heifers in calf	756	848	787	763	718	701
Total sheep and lambs		44 392	42 823	44 471	44 656	42 264	36 716
of which:	ewes and shearlings (g)	..	20 696	21 260	21 458	20 449	17 921
	lambs under one year old	22 400	21 032	22 138	22 092	20 857	17 769
Total pigs		7 650	8 072	8 146	7 284	6 482	5 845
of which:	sows in pig and other sows for breeding	681	683	675	603	537	527
	gilts in pig	110	116	103	85	73	71
Total fowl (h)		126 075	161 892	147 609	149 867	154 504	163 875
of which:	table fowl including broilers	74 601	106 937	98 244	101 625	105 689	112 531
	laying fowl (i)	..	34 286	29 483	29 258	28 687	29 895
	growing pullets	10 827	11 510	9 860	9 583	9 461	9 367

source: DEFRA Statistics

(a) For various reasons, the crop area figures and livestock numbers shown in this table may differ slightly from those shown in chapter 5.

(b) From 2000 Scottish minor holdings have been included; data for earlier years are therefore not directly comparable.

(c) England and Wales only prior to 1992.

(d) Includes non-commercial orchards.

(e) Includes wine grapes.

(f) Hardy nursery stock, bulbs and flowers.

(g) Improvements to the questions on sheep were introduced in 1995; data for earlier years are therefore not directly comparable.

(h) Improvements to the Census methodology were introduced in 1997 onwards to account for poultry production on unregistered units. Consequently the figures from 1997 onwards are not directly comparable with preceding years results.

(I) Excludes fowls laying eggs for hatching.

TABLE 3.3 Numbers and sizes of holdings

Enquiries: Miles Templeton on 01904 455306   email: miles.h.templeton@defra.gsi.gov.uk

The data in this table exclude minor holdings for Great Britain. In Northern Ireland all active farms are included.(a)

At June of each year

		1995		2000	
		Number of holdings ('000)	Percent of total ESU	Number of holdings ('000)	Percent of total ESU
Size of holding (ESU) (b)	under 8 ESU	103.0	2.9	112.3	2.7
	8 to under 40 ESU	68.1	16.3	60.8	14.6
	40 to under 100 ESU	42.5	31.3	38.0	28.8
	100 to under 200 ESU	15.7	24.6	15.9	25.6
	200ESU and over	5.7	25.0	6.3	28.2
	Total	234.9	100.0	233.2	100.0
	Average size (ESUs):				
	All holdings		36.8		36.3
	Holdings 8 ESU and over		63.6		68.1
		Number of holdings ('000)	Hectares ('000)	Number of holdings ('000)	Hectares ('000)
Total area on holdings (b)	Under 20 hectares	95.6	812	107.2	724
	20 to under 50 hectares	57.7	1 902	48.2	1 597
	50 to under 100 hectares	41.2	2 927	37.1	2 648
	100 hectares and over	40.5	11 359	40.7	11 571
	Total	234.9	16 999	233.2	16 540
	Average area (ha):				
	All holdings		72.4		70.9
	Holdings 8 ESU and over		113.2		119.1
	% of total area on holdings with 100 hectares and over		66.8		70.0
		Number of holdings ('000)	Hectares ('000)	Number of holdings ('000)	Hectares ('000)
Tillage and grass area (b) (c) (d)	0.1 to under 20 hectares	95.0	796	97.3	699
	20 to under 50 hectares	58.1	1 915	48.7	1 611
	50 to under 100 hectares	40.3	2 842	36.3	2 584
	100hectares and over	30.0	5 775	31.3	6 202
	Total	223.3	11 329	213.6	11 096
	Average crops and grass area per holding (hectares) (e)		50.7		52.0
	% of total crops and grass area on holdings with 100 hectares and over		51.0		55.9

source: DEFRA Statistics

(a) From 1997 the Northern Ireland census was based on an improved register of holdings and included all active farms having one or more hectares of farmed land plus any below that size which had significant agricultural output.

(b) Land in Great Britain let out under short term lets is attributed to the lessor, but land so let out in Northern Ireland (under the conacre system) is now attributed to the lessee. This difference affects both the number of holdings and their average size.

(c) The numbers of holdings shown in this part of the table are lower than those presented in the "total area" part of the table because holdings without crops and grass are excluded.

(d) The areas shown in this part of the table exclude set-aside land.

(e) Refers to holdings with crops and grass.

TABLE 3.4 Numbers and sizes of enterprises

Enquiries: Miles Templeton on 01904 455306   email: miles.h.templeton@defra.gsi.gov.uk

The data in this table exclude minor holdings in Great Britain. In Northern Ireland all active farms are included. (a)

Areas refer to the area of the specified crop and not to the area of the holding

At June of each year

		1995		2000	
		Number of holdings ('000)	Hectares ('000)	Number of holdings ('000)	Hectares ('000)
Cereals (excluding maize)	0.1 to under 20.0 hectares	34.4	302	28.3	259
	20.0 to under 50.0 hectares	18.8	612	16.0	524
	50.0 hectares and over	19.6	2 262	20.7	2 560
	Total	72.7	3 176	65.0	3 344
	Average area (hectares)(b)		43.7		51.4
	% of total cereals area on holdings with 50.0 hectares and over		71.2		76.6
Oilseed rape	0.1 to under 20.0 hectares	8.7	92	7.3	80
	20.0 to under 50.0 hectares	4.8	146	4.4	135
	50.0 hectares and over	1.5	116	1.4	118
	Total	4.9	354	13.1	332
	Average area (hectares)(b)		23.7		25.5
	% of total oilseed rape area on holdings with 50.0 hectares and over		32.7		35.6
Sugar beet (England and Wales only)	0.1 to under 10.0 hectares	3.9	22	3.3	19
	10.0 to under 20.0 hectares	2.7	38	2.4	34
	20.0 hectares and over	3.1	136	2.8	119
	Total	9.7	196	8.6	173
	Average area (hectares)(b)		20.2		20.2
	% of total sugar beet area on holdings with 20.0 hectares and over		69.5		69.1
Potatoes	0.1 to under 10.0 hectares	14.4	42	9.5	29
	10.0 to under 20.0 hectares	2.9	41	2.6	37
	20.0 hectares and over	2.3	87	2.3	100
	Total	19.6	169	14.4	166
	Average area (hectares)(b)		8.6		11.5
	% of total potato area on holdings with 20.0 hectares and over		51.3		60.2
	holdings	Number of livestock ('000)	Number of holdings ('000)	Number of livestock ('000)	Number of ('000)
Dairy cows	1 to 49 dairy cows	17.4	468	12.8	316
	50 to 99	13.7	973	11.0	793
	100 and over	7.8	1 159	8.0	1 226
	Total	38.9	2 600	31.9	2 335
	Average size of herd		66.8		73.3
	% of total dairy cows in herds of 100 and over		44.6		52.5

continued

TABLE 3.4 *cont.*

Areas refer to the area of the specified crop and not to the area of the holding

At June of each year

		1995		2000	
Beef cows	1 to 19 beef cows	42.9	329	36.9	297
	20 to 49	18.2	565	18.0	563
	50 and over	9.9	891	10.5	969
	Total	71.0	1 786	65.4	1 829
	Average size of herd		25.2		28.0
	% of total beef cows in herds				
	of 50 and over		49.9		53.0
Sheep breeding flock	1 to 99 breeding sheep	38.4	1 599	35.1	1 432
	100 to 499	34.4	7 983	31.6	7 479
	500 and over	10.8	9 786	11.2	10 520
	Total	83.6	19 369	77.9	19 432
	Average size of flock		231.6		249.4
	% of total breeding sheep in flocks				
	of 500 and over		50.5		54.1
Pig breeding herd	1 to 49 breeding pigs	6.6	63	5.0	41
	50 to 99	0.9	66	0.6	39
	100 and over	2.1	613	1.5	527
	Total	9.7	742	7.1	607
	Average size of herd		76.7		85.4
	% of total breeding pigs in herds				
	of 100 and over		82.6		86.8
Fattening pigs	1 to 199 fattening pigs	6.1	247	4.9	158
(Fattening pigs of over 20kg	200 to 999	2.9	1 437	2.0	1 043
liveweight excluding barren sows)	1,000 and over	1.3	2 942	1.2	2 840
	Total	10.3	4 626	8.1	4 041
	Average size of herd		450.7		501.3
	% of total fattening pigs in herds				
	of 1,000 and over		63.6		70.3
Broilers	1 to 9,999 broilers	1.2	921	0.8	687
(Includes small numbers of other table	10,000 to 99,999	0.8	33 457	0.9	36 656
fowl in Scotland and Northern Ireland)	100,000 and over	0.2	42 199	0.3	67 960
	Total	2.3	76 577	2.0	105 303
	Average size of flock		33 869		53 508
	% of total broilers in flock				
	of 100,000 and over		55.1		64.5
Laying fowls	1 to 4,999 laying fowls	27.7	2 574	23.8	2 056
	5,000 to 19,999	0.6	5 919	0.6	5 671
	20,000 and over	0.3	31 154	0.3	28 821
	Total	28.6	39 648	24.7	36 548
	Average size of flock		1 385		1 482
	% of total laying fowls in flocks				
	of 20,000 and over		78.6		78.9

source: DEFRA Statistics

(a) Figures for 2000 are not directly comparable with those for 1995 because improvements were introduced in 1997 to census methodology to account for production on unregistered units.

(b) Average area refers to the average area of the specified crop on holdings that grow that crop. Holdings that do not grow the crop are excluded from the calculation.

2001

TABLE 3.5 Labour force in agriculture

Enquiries:Lindsey Clothier 01904 455319   email: lindsey.j.clothier@defra.gsi.gov.uk

The data cover main and minor holdings in the United Kingdom (a) to (e)

Thousand persons

At June of each year

	Average of 1990-92	1998	1999	2000	2001(a)	2001(b)
Workers						
Regular whole-time:						
male	105	88	82	73	69	70
female	15	13	12	10	11	11
Total	120	101	94	84	80	82
Regular part-time: (f)						
male	30	30	27	25	22	23
female	27	25	22	21	19	19
Total	57	54	50	45	41	42
Seasonal or casual:						
male	55	54	51	46	45	45
female	33	25	21	18	19	19
Salaried managers (g)	8	12	14	11	13	14
Total workers	272	245	230	204	198	202
Farmers, partners, directors and spouses						
whole-time	. .	184	177	169	166	168
part-time (f)	. .	179	179	183	186	198
Total farmers, partners, directors and spouses	372	363	356	353	352	367
Total labour force (including farmers and their spouses) (h)&(i)	645	608	586	557	550	568

source: DEFRA Statistics

(a) These results exclude the effect of the register improvement in England and are directly comparable with June 2000.

(b) These results include the effect of the register improvement in England and are NOT directly comparable with June 2000.

(c) From 1997 the Northern Ireland census was based on an improved register of farm businesses and included all active farms having one or more hectares of farmed land plus any below that size which had significant agricultural output.

(d) Results from 1998 are not consistent with previous years, due to changes in the labour questions on the June Agricultural and Horticultural Census, and due to revisions made to English and Welsh results.

(e) From 1998 for England and Wales, estimates for holdings which have not been recording labour have been made, apart from economically insignificant holdings which are very unlikely to be in commercial production. An offsetting adjustment has been made to take out any labour being recorded on these very small holdings. The net effect has been to reduce the level of the labour series between 1998 and 2000 by about 5,000. This has not affected the trends previously recorded.

(f) Part-time is defined as less than 39 hours per week in England and Wales, less than 38 hours per week in Scotland and less than 30 hours per week in Northern Ireland.

(g) From 1998 in England and Wales, all farmers managing holdings for limited companies or other institutions were asked to classify themselves as salaried managers.

(h) This is the series referred to as 'Workforce in agriculture' in Table 2.2.

(i) Figures exclude schoolchildren and most trainees.

TABLE 3.6 Fixed capital stock of agriculture (a)

Enquiries: Jane Hinton on 020 7270 8612 email: jane.hinton@defra.gsi.gov.uk

At end year

	Average of 1990-92	1997	1998	1999	2000	2001 (provisional)
Gross capital stock (1995 = 100)						
Buildings and works	99.9	98.6	97.4	95.4	93.2	..
Plant and machinery	101.1	100.	97.6	95.	92.2	..
Vehicles	94.4	103.8	102.9	101.8	101.2	..
Total	99.7	99.2	97.7	95.5	93.2	90.9

source: DEFRA Statistics

(a) Excludes livestock capital assets.

Chapter **4** Prices

Price indices
(Table 4.1)

1 Table 4.1 shows price indices for agricultural products and inputs. Chart 4.1 portrays the main changes in these indices over recent years. Between 2000 and 2001 the average price of agricultural products rose by 7.0 per cent and inputs rose by 3.6 per cent. Product prices have fallen 6.3 per cent since 1997, whereas the average price of inputs have remained largely unchanged.

2 In 2001, the price of crop products rose by 11 per cent mainly due to an increase in the price of cereals, root crops, fresh vegetables, oilseeds, hay and straw. The price of livestock and livestock products rose by 5.2 per cent with significant increases in the prices of milk (13 per cent) and eggs (6.5 per cent). Livestock (for slaughter and export) prices rose by 1.2 per cent.

3 It should be noted that these indices are constructed using fixed annual weights (relating to 1995). They reflect observed market prices and do not take account of direct subsidy payments. In contrast, the price changes presented in table 6.2, derived from the aggregate accounts, include subsidy payments and are based on current production. For these reasons the price movements presented here and in Chapter 6 differ.

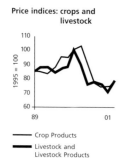

Price indices: crops and livestock

— Crop Products
— Livestock and Livestock Products

Chart 4.1
Price indices for products and inputs

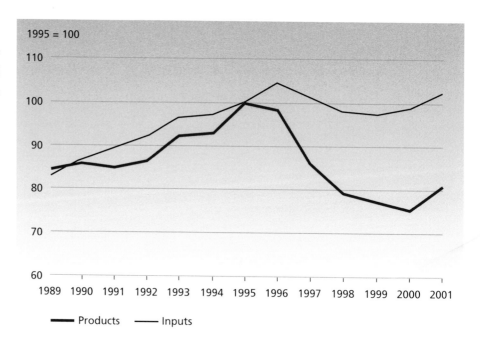

— Products   — Inputs

Farm rents
(Table 4.2)

4 Table 4.2 shows indices of average rents per hectare. The rents refer to the calendar year, whilst the surveys on which they are based are conducted in October. Because of the duration of periods for rent settings, the values applying to the calendar year are deemed to be mainly (approximately 75 per cent) a carry over from those recorded in the preceding October. Therefore the derivation of the changes (noted

2001

below) are driven primarily by developments in 2000 and only to a lesser extent (approximately 25 per cent) by conditions in 2001.

5 For Great Britain as a whole, provisional results for 2001 suggest a decrease in average rents of around 2 per cent. Average rents decreased in England by around 3 per cent. In contrast rents in Scotland and Wales have increased. Provisional results for Northern Ireland indicate a drop of around 1 per cent.

6 In England and Wales average rent estimates for the Full Agricultural Tenancies (FATs) series were based on results of the former annual Rent Enquiry (RE) for years up to and including 1995 and thereafter on the Annual Survey of Tenanted Land (ASTL). To ensure consistency with the earlier Rent Enquiry (RE) series, a weighted average of the RE and FATs rents derived from the ASTL is taken for 1995 to 1997 (with an increasing incremental weighting on the ASTL). From 1998 the series is derived exclusively from the ASTL. Estimates of average rents in 2001 in England and Wales have been derived from a very small sample of ASTL returns and are thus purely provisional and will be subject to review when more robust estimates become available.

7 For Scotland, up to 1995, rent estimates were based on the results of continuing Field Enquiries. After its demise that year, they were based on the Farm Accounts Survey, and from 1998 on a new Survey of Tenanted Land.

8 In Northern Ireland virtually all land is let in "conacre", i.e. nominally short-term lettings (for 11 months or 364 days), although in practice some can be extended beyond this. The estimates are based on results from the Northern Ireland Farm Business Survey.

Agricultural land prices
(Table 4.3 and Chart 4.2)

9 The average prices of all sales shown in table 4.3 are obtained from data on land transfers collected by the Valuation Office Agency in Great Britain and the Valuation and Lands Agency in Northern Ireland. Only a very small proportion of the total area of farmland in the UK is sold in any particular year. The average price of land sold can therefore be subject to considerable variation from year to year, and in the case of unweighted averages shown here, may vary with size and type of lot sold in the year concerned. Chart 4.2 plots the average price in real terms of all sales of agricultural land from 1993-2000.

Chart 4.2 Price of agriculture land (all sales) at 2000 prices

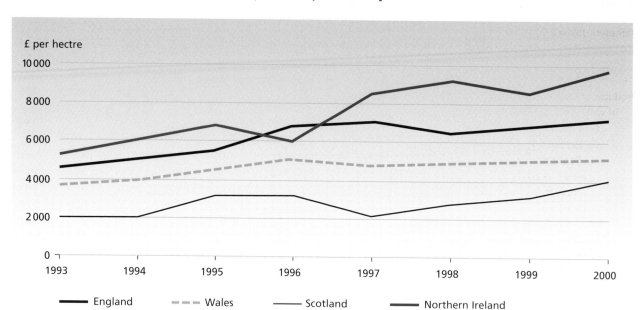

10 Recent data on land prices in Scotland should be treated with care given the substantial lags in gathering data. However, the available information on Scottish land sales suggests that average prices for all farm types rose into 2000 after many types had seen falling prices in 1997 and, to a lesser extent, 1998. The upward trend in prices was somewhat unexpected given continuing depressed farm incomes and may suggest that subsidies are being capitalised into land values or that non-agricultural users are supporting land prices. Preliminary indications for 2001 suggest that, although the level of land sales was low, prices held up well.

11 The average price of agricultural land in Wales has increased by 17 per cent (8.3 per cent in real terms) over the period 1997 to 2000. This increase has occurred steadily over the period although it should be noted that a relatively small number of high (or low) value transactions can sometimes have a disproportionate effect on this average.

12 In England provisional figures show that land prices were 7.2 per cent (4.2 per cent in real terms) higher in 2000 compared with 1999. This overall rise in price is a result of differing trends. For example, there were significant rises in the average price of grade 4 and 5 land (up 38 per cent) and ungraded land (up 75 per cent) whereas the price of grade 1 and 2 land fell by 4.1 per cent. The price of land in Yorkshire and the Humber fell by 9.8 per cent, but rose in the North West (up 27 per cent) and the South West (up 15 per cent). The decline in number of sales and area sold, which began in 1998, continued. In 2000 sales were down 34 per cent compared with 1997, and area sold down 46 per cent.

13 The number of land sales recorded each year in Northern Ireland has been declining markedly. Most sales involve relatively small areas and, though variable, the long term trend in prices is upward.

TABLE 4.1 Price indices for products and inputs

Enquiries: Allan Howsam on 01904 455253   email: allan.howsam@defra.gsi.gov.uk

Indices(a): 1995=100   *Annual average figures for calendar years*

	Average of 1990-92	1997	1998	1999	2000	2001 (provisional)
Producer prices for agricultural products (b)	85.7	85.9	79.1	76.8	75.2	80.5
of which:						
Crop products:	87.1	76.4	77.2	75.5	71.1	79.2
Cereals	100.2	79.3	68.3	66.5	59.9	65.0
Root crops	52.2	39.0	56.3	57.9	44.1	56.0
Fresh vegetables	88.9	90.9	96.8	90.5	94.9	106.5
Fresh fruit	104.9	105.6	99.6	93.8	101.5	99.2
Seeds	94.1	78.9	77.4	67.2	56.1	56.4
Flowers and plants	94.2	103.9	104.0	107.4	103.6	102.9
Other crop products	94.3	81.2	85.7	82.8	87.3	105.8
Livestock and livestock products:	85.4	90.5	77.0	74.0	74.3	78.2
Livestock (for slaughter and export)	88.7	91.3	76.2	74.3	78.2	79.1
Milk	77.8	88.7	77.7	73.6	67.9	76.8
Eggs	106.6	94.6	83.3	74.1	75.9	80.8
Other livestock products	82.8	88.9	74.4	71.1	69.8	73.4
Prices of agricultural inputs:	89.5	101.2	98.0	97.1	98.6	102.2
of which:						
Currently consumed in agriculture:	89.6	100.1	95.8	94.6	96.6	101.1
Livestock feedingstuffs	94.3	97.1	83.0	77.1	77.5	85.1
Seeds	94.6	89.4	91.7	83.2	76.1	76.2
Fertilisers and soil improvers	92.0	97.3	86.2	83.4	88.0	102.1
Plant protection products	91.5	105.7	98.0	96.4	89.9	87.7
Maintenance and repair of plant and machinery	83.6	109.3	112.5	116.6	120.9	126.2
Energy, lubricants	93.7	103.4	94.5	102.6	127.6	123.8
Maintenance and repair of buildings	86.6	102.6	103.8	102.8	105.3	107.3
Veterinary services	97.4	102.3	103.5	103.8	102.8	100.8
General expenses	84.5	99.9	105.5	109.4	112.4	117.8
Contributing to agricultural investment (c):	88.8	106.6	108.5	108.8	108.6	107.2
Machinery and other equipment	89.7	107.6	109.0	109.4	107.8	105.0
Buildings	86.1	103.7	107.0	107.4	111.0	113.6

source: DEFRA Statistics website, www.defra.gov.uk/esg

(a) Indices covering an aggregation of commodities are weighted averages with weights based on the values of output of the respective commodities in 1995.

(b) These indices reflect prices received by producers but exclude direct subsidies.

(c) Covers the purchase and maintenance of capital items, but excludes stocks.

TABLE 4.2 Farm rents

Enquiries: John Walsh on 020 7270 8795   email: john.walsh@defra.gsi.gov.uk

Average per hectare: indices, 1995=100

Calendar years

		Average of 1990-92	1997	1998	1999	2000	2001 (provisional)
England:	FATs (a)	94.8	110.6	114.0	112.7	112.4	107.4
	Average (b)	..	109.8	117.3	119.8	117.9	114.6
Wales:	FATs (a)	87.7	121.3	119.6	113.0	113.2	111.8
	Average (b)	..	114.6	126.1	126.1	129.1	136.3
Scotland (c)		..	117.5	121.0	123.5	128.5	130.0
Great Britain		90.0	110.7	118.3	120.6	119.5	117.3
Northern Ireland (d)		81.4	107.7	105.1	100.5	93.3	92.3

source: DEFRA Statistics website, www.defra.gov.uk/esg

(a) See text.

(b) A new series for England and Wales has been introduced giving a weighted average rent £/ha for all agreements over a year in length.

(c) Scottish estimates relate to crops and grassland only. From 1998 onwards Crops and Grass is replaced by a Non-LFA classification.

(d) See text.

TABLE 4.3 Agricultural land prices

Enquiries: Barbara Boize on 01904 455081   email: barbara.boize@defra.gsi.gov.uk

£ per hectare

Calendar years

	Average of 1990-92	1997	1998	1999	2000
England (a) (b)					
All sales	4 051	6 451	6 140	6 659	7 139
Wales (a) (b)					
All sales	3 230	4 376	4 711	4 875	5 125
Scotland (a)					
All sales	2 375	1 926	2 609	3 045	3 967
Northern Ireland (a) (c)					
All sales	3 351	7 858	8 746	8 267	9 634

source: DEFRA Statistics website, www.defra.gov.uk/esg

(a) These series, based on Inland Revenue data, exclude land sold for non-agricultural purposes. In Great Britain sales of less than 5 hectares, and in Northern Ireland of less than 2 hectares, are also excluded. Data are subject to retrospective revision.

(b) From 1993, figures for England and Wales are not directly comparable with those estimated in previous years because some observations influenced by non-market considerations are now excluded.

(c) or Northern Ireland there is a delay, thought to average about 3 months, between the date on which a sale is agreed and the date on which it is included in the analysis. From 1990, figures are not directly comparable with those estimated in previous years.

Chapter **5** Commodities

Summary **1** The value of production (including subsidies directly related to products) was 0.7 per cent or £104 million higher at current prices in 2001. In this chapter the volume of production corresponds to the quantities of sales of products. It differs from the accounting concept of volume in chapter 6 which includes changes in work-in-progress and treats changes in quality as changes in volume.

- The total value of production of *cereals* fell by 14 per cent to £2,019 million. Although prices recovered from the low levels of 2000, a fall in both area and yields led to an overall fall in production of 21 per cent. Within this total the value of production for *wheat* fell by 23 per cent, whilst that of *barley* increased by 6.0 per cent.

- The cost of *purchased feedingstuffs* rose by £189 million or 9.0 per cent to £2,297 million. The increase was largely due to higher levels of compound feed production with the dairy sector showing the largest increase.

- The value of production of *oilseed rape* rose by £29 million (12 per cent) to £275 million as a result of an increase in the planted area and higher prices.

- The value of production of *linseed* fell by £18 million (53 per cent) to £16 million as a result of a 58 per cent decrease in the planted area and a reduction in the value of subsidy rates.

- Overall production of *potatoes* fell in 2001 by 1.9 per cent, but with higher prices than in 2000, the value of production rose by 32 per cent to £600 million. As the 2001 harvest got underway, and more stocks became available, prices fell but remained at higher levels than those achieved after the 2000 harvest.

- The value of production of all *horticultural commodities* rose by 8.1 per cent, to £1,921 million in 2001 with price rises due to a shortage of supply. The value of production for vegetables increased by 11 per cent, while fruit increased by 6.6 per cent and ornamentals rose by 5.3 per cent.

- The value of production of *cattle and calves* fell by 9.5 per cent in 2001 to £1,809 million. This reflected the large fall in the production of beef and veal due to foot and mouth disease.

- The value of production of *sheep and lambs* fell by 35 per cent to £625 million in 2001 reflecting a large fall in the production of mutton and lamb due mainly to foot and mouth disease and a large fall in direct subsidy payments.

- The value of production of *pigs* fell by 5.4 per cent in 2001 to £751 million. This reflected a fall in production due largely to the contraction of the breeding herd in the previous year.

- The value of production of *poultrymeat* increased by £13 million or 1.0 per cent. The volume of production increased by 3.4 per cent. Poultrymeat prices

2001

decreased during 2001, with broilers dropping by 0.8 pence to 70.0 pence per kilogram.

- The value of production of *livestock products* (principally milk and eggs) rose by 16 per cent overall. Milk rose by 18 per cent to £2,818 million largely due to a 13 per cent increase in the average milk price received by farmers, while the value of production of eggs for human consumption increased by 9.5 per cent due to an increase in the volume of production.

Structure of Tables **2** Each of the main commodity tables is divided, where appropriate, into three sections:

Production

For crops the aggregate areas and average yields are shown and are used to derive the levels of production. For livestock the populations, marketings and average slaughter weights are shown and lead to estimates of production. Value of production figures are broken down into sales out of the industry, sales within the industry, changes in stocks or work-in-progress and subsidies (less taxes) on production. The value of production in these tables is the same as the value of output in table 6.1.

Prices

Average producer prices and/or selected market prices are provided.

Supply and Use

Total new supply is defined as production plus imports less exports. Overseas Trade Statistics are provided by H.M. Customs and Excise.

Total domestic use is the total new supply adjusted for changes in stocks. Where stocks are insignificant or not known the total domestic use is assumed to be the same as the total new supply.

Production as percentage of total new supply for use in the UK gives an indication of the self-sufficiency of the UK in the commodity.

Cereals

Cereals **3** The total value of production of cereals fell by 14 per cent to £2,019 million. The
(Tables 5.1-5.4) very wet winter and poor growing conditions in the spring affected plantings and yields. Plantings of wheat and winter barley fell sharply whilst the areas of spring barley, oilseed rape and set-aside increased. The total area of cereals fell by 10 per cent and overall yields for cereals were down 12 per cent.

Monthly cereal price index

Wheat 4 The value of wheat production decreased by 23 per cent to £1,222 million, with a
(Table 5.2) fall in production volume partially offset by the recovery in prices. Production fell
as a result of reduced plantings (down 22 per cent) and lower yields, caused by the
very wet winter and poor growing conditions in the spring. Subsidies also fell and
were 24 per cent lower than the previous year. Prices increased by 13 per cent in
2001, with the market moving to import parity in response to the smaller harvest,
and increased demand for animal feeding caused by foot and mouth disease
movement restrictions. Exports fell by 54 per cent as a result of the lower
availability of supply, higher internal prices and competition from other suppliers.

Barley 5 The value of barley production rose by 6.0 per cent in 2001 to £726 million. This
(Table 5.3) was due to a 3.2 per cent increase in the volume of production, an increase of 5.9
per cent in subsidies and a 3.1 per cent increase in price. Intervention stocks have
fallen to 11 thousand tonnes, their lowest levels since 1996. Exports decreased by
over 63 per cent in 2001 as a result of competition from other supplies and
increased internal demand due to rising wheat prices.

Oats 6 The value of oats production fell by 0.6 per cent in 2001 to £64 million. A fall in
(Table 5.4) production was offset by a recovery in prices. Volume of production fell by 3.9 per
cent with a fall in yield offsetting a slight increase in area. Average prices increased
by almost 5 per cent. Usage in 2001 increased by over 3 per cent, whilst lower
availability has reduced exports by around 16 per cent.

TABLE 5.1 Total cereals

Enquiries: Alex Clothier on 01904 455068   email: alex.clothier@defra.gsi.gov.uk

Thousand tonnes (unless otherwise specified)   *Calendar years*

	Average of 1990-92	1997	1998	1999	2000	2001 (provisional)
Production						
Area ('000 hectares)	3 550	3 514	3 420	3 141	3 348	3 013
Volume of harvested production	22 426	23 530	22 790	22 120	23 990	18 990
Value of production (£ million) (a)	2 439	2 907	2 502	2 326	2 338	2 019
Supply and Use						
Imports from: the EU	2 248	2 005	2 017	1 677	1 668	1 750
the rest of the world	585	795	739	926	917	969
Exports to: the EU	3 696	3 751	4 392	3 040	3 634	1 840
the rest of the world	2 510	1 728	1 418	1 360	1 995	630
Total new supply	19 052	20 851	19 737	20 324	20 945	19 239
Increase in farm and other stocks	- 64	588	- 683	- 41	479	- 1 577
Total domestic uses	19 118	20 263	20 419	20 365	20 466	20 816
Production as % of total new supply for use in UK	118%	113%	115%	109%	115%	99%

source: DEFRA Statistics website, www.defra.gov.uk/esg

(a) Includes Arable Area Payments, but excludes set-aside payments
and farm saved seed. Taxes where applicable are deducted.

TABLE 5.2 Wheat

Enquiries: Alex Clothier on 01904 455068   email: alex.clothier@defra.gsi.gov.uk

Thousand tonnes (unless otherwise specified)

Calendar years

	Average of 1990-92	1997	1998	1999	2000	2001 (provisional)
Production						
Area ('000 hectares)	2 020	2 036	2 045	1 847	2 086	1 635
Yield (tonnes/hectare)	7.01	7.38	7.56	8.05	8.01	7.08
Volume of harvested production	14 164	15 020	15 470	14 870	16 700	11 570
Value of production (£ million) (a)	1 599	1 851	1 652	1 525	1 580	1 222
of which: sales	1 538	1 287	1 126	1 061	1 003	1 056
subsidies (b)	- 60	493	466	420	458	349
on farm use	90	77	79	64	33	38
change in stocks	31	- 7	- 18	- 20	86	- 221
Prices (c)						
Milling wheat (£/tonne)	130	101	84	81	74	82
Feed wheat (£/tonne)	114	89	75	73	66	75
Supply and Use						
Production	14 163	15 020	15 470	14 870	16 700	11 570
Imports from: the EU	661	752	779	579	556	594
the rest of the world	303	413	471	616	621	664
Exports to: the EU	2 547	2 719	3 566	2 598	2 957	1 310
the rest of the world	1 666	1 001	643	255	714	380
Total new supply	10 915	12 465	12 511	13 212	14 205	11 138
Increase in farm and other stocks	35	- 225	- 408	32	1 075	- 2 118
Total domestic uses	10 880	12 690	12 919	13 180	13 130	13 256
of which: flour milling	4 922	5 535	5 707	5 668	5 617	5 627
animal feed	4 704	5 955	6 117	6 367	6 460	6 480
seed	340	368	332	375	265	330
other uses and waste	914	833	763	769	788	819
Production as % of total new supply for use in UK	130%	120%	124%	113%	118%	104%
% of home grown wheat in milling grist	86%	84%	80%	83%	82%	85%

Wheat (Crop Years: July–June)

Thousand tonnes (unless otherwise specified)

	1996/97	1997/98	1998/99	1999/00	2000/01
Production and output					
Volume of harvested production	16 100	15 020	15 470	14 870	16 700
Value of production (£ million) (a)	2 163	1 762	1 593	1 509	1 534
of which: sales	1 537	1 179	1 075	1 033	1 069
subsidies (b)	507	493	466	420	458
on farm use	72	81	80	47	21
change in stocks	48	8	- 29	9	- 14

source: DEFRA Statistics website, www.defra.gov.uk/esg

(a) Excludes farm saved seed

(b) Includes Arable Area Payments but excludes set-aside payments. Net of Taxes. The negative values from 1986 to 1992 reflect levy payments made by producers under the Cereals Co-responsibility Scheme.

(c) Average prices weighted by volumes of sales

TABLE 5.3 Barley

Enquiries: Alex Clothier on 01904 455068   email: alex.clothier@defra.gsi.gov.uk

Thousand tonnes (unless otherwise specified) — *Calendar years*

	Average of 1990-92	1997	1998	1999	2000	2001 (provisional)
Production						
Area ('000 hectares)	1 404	1 359	1 255	1 179	1 128	1 244
Yield (tonnes/hectare)	5.46	5.76	5.28	5.58	5.75	5.49
Volume of harvested production	7 634	7 830	6 630	6 580	6 490	6 700
Value of production (£ million) (a)	782	977	781	735	685	726
of which: sales	603	421	397	308	317	268
subsidies (b)	- 23	316	277	259	244	259
on farm use	249	193	164	148	136	144
change in stocks	- 47	47	- 57	20	- 12	56
Prices (c)						
Malting barley (£/tonne)	126	92	85	79	75	76
Feed barley (£/tonne)	111	80	71	70	65	68
Supply and Use						
Production	7 634	7 830	6 630	6 580	6 490	6 700
Imports from: the EU	231	118	154	107	50	77
the rest of the world	-	26	31	22	20	24
Exports to: the EU	1 089	941	768	399	550	430
the rest of the world	844	727	775	1 105	1 281	250
Total new supply	5 933	6 307	5 271	5 205	4 729	6 121
Increase in farm and other stocks	- 81	808	- 278	- 72	- 626	538
Total domestic uses	6 014	5 499	5 549	5 277	5 355	5 583
or which: brewing/distilling	1 871	1 938	1 999	1 910	1 925	1 939
animal feed	3 800	3 297	3 304	3 129	3 199	3 429
seed	198	213	200	192	187	169
other uses and waste	146	51	45	45	44	46
Production as % of total new supply for use in UK	129%	124%	126%	126%	137%	109%

Barley (Crop Years: July-June)

Thousand tonnes (unless otherwise specified)

	1996/97	1997/98	1998/99	1999/00	2000/01
Production and output					
Volume of harvested production	7 790	7 830	6 630	6 580	6 490
Value of production (£ million) (a)	1 148	925	766	724	690
of which: sales	624	435	339	323	298
subsidies (b)	314	316	277	259	244
on farm use	195	175	155	141	140
change in stocks	15	- 1	- 4	1	7

source: DEFRA Statistics website, www.defra.gov.uk/esg

(a) Excludes farm saved seed

(b) Includes Arable Area Payments but excludes set-aside payments. Net of Taxes. The negative values from 1986 to 1992 reflect levy payments made by producers under the Cereals Co-Responsibility Scheme.

(c) Average prices weighted by volumes of sales

TABLE 5.4 Oats

Enquiries: Alex Clothier on 01904 455068   email: alex.clothier@defra.gsi.gov.uk

Thousand tonnes (unless otherwise specified)   *Calendar years*

	Average of 1990-92	1997	1998	1999	2000	2001 (provisional)
Production						
Area ('000 hectares)	104	100	98	92	109	112
Yield (tonnes/hectare)	5.00	5.76	5.98	5.87	5.87	5.60
Volume of harvested production	518	575	585	540	640	615
Value of production (£ million) (a)	54	71	61	58	65	64
of which: sales:	38	35	25	24	27	27
subsidies (b)	- 2	23	22	20	23	23
on farm use	20	12	12	14	12	12
change in stocks	- 3	1	2	- 1	2	2
Prices (c)						
Milling oats (£/tonne)	113	83	66	71	64	68
Feed oats (£/tonne)	110	76	62	71	64	66
Supply and Use						
Production	518	575	585	540	640	615
Imports from: the EU	7	16	11	11	7	5
the rest of the world	-	-	-	2	-	-
Exports to: the EU	35	78	54	34	107	90
the rest of the world	-	-	-	-	-	-
Total new supply	490	513	542	518	540	530
Increase in farm and other stocks	- 17	6	3	- 2	30	3
Total domestic uses	507	507	539	520	510	527
of which: milling	226	259	272	266	261	282
animal feed	244	227	246	229	231	227
seed	21	19	18	21	16	16
other uses and waste	16	3	3	4	3	3
Production as % of total new supply for use in UK	106%	112%	108%	104%	119%	116%

source: DEFRA Statistics website, www.defra.gov.uk/esg

(a) Excludes farm saved seed

(b) Includes Arable Area Payments but excludes set-aside payments. Net of Taxes. The negative values from 1986 to 1992 reflect levy payments made by producers under the Cereals Co-Responsibility Scheme.

(c) Average prices weighted by volumes of sales

Other crops

Oilseed rape 7
(Table 5.5)

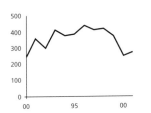

OSR Valuation in £ million

The value of production increased by 12 per cent to £275 million. The area planted rose by 12 per cent but yields were down on last year. This led to a slight overall increase in the volume of production of 0.2 per cent. There has also been a recovery in prices to levels not seen since January 1999. A reduction in the subsidy rate contributed to an overall reduction in the total subsidy paid of 5.6 per cent.

Linseed 8
(Table 5.6)

The value of production fell by 53 per cent to £16 million. The area planted was 58 per cent lower than in 2000, and in spite of a recovery in yields, volume of production fell by 10 per cent to 39,000 tonnes. A reduction in the subsidy rate and in claimed area led to a fall in the value of the Arable Area Payments Scheme subsidy, down 65 per cent to £10 million.

Sugar beet and sugar 9
(Table 5.7)

The overall value of production rose by 1.2 per cent to £255 million. The area of contracted sugar beet was increased in line with quota but overall yield was down. The very wet winter led to poor quality seedbeds and the wet spring delayed plantings. The resultant 9.9 per cent fall in volume of beet production has been offset by a 12 per cent increase in price. Sugar production from beet fell by 9.4 per cent to 1.2 million tonnes.

Potatoes 10
(Table 5.8)

Northern Ireland data has been revised back to 1981 in line with changes made last year.

11 The total area for all potatoes fell by 0.1 per cent in 2001 with the area for earlies falling by 39 per cent. This was brought about by the declining market for earlies and the delayed planting due to rain. The area for maincrop rose by 3.0 per cent. The overall production in 2001 was down by 1.9 per cent, but with higher prices than in 2000, the value of production rose by 32 per cent. Prices increased from £117.14 per tonne in January 2001, to a high of £164.92 in May, remaining fairly high until August, then falling back to end the year at £88.49.

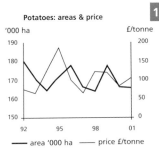

Potatoes: areas & price

area '000 ha   — price £/tonne

Peas and beans for stockfeed 12
(Table 5.9)

The combined value of production for peas and beans for stockfeed rose by 26 per cent to £141 million. The area of dried peas grown for stockfeed increased by over 12,000 hectares in 2001 and despite a small drop in yields, production rose by 13 per cent to 280,000 tonnes. The area of field beans grown for stockfeed increased by over 44,000 hectares in 2001 and despite a drop in yields, production rose by 22 per cent to 590,000 tonnes. The combined value of subsidies for 2001 rose 16 per cent to £63 million.

Table 5.5 Oilseed rape

Enquiries: Dave Fernall on 01904 455058   email: david.fernall@defra.gsi.gov.uk

Thousand tonnes (unless otherwise specified)   *Calendar years*

	Average of 1990-92	1997	1998	1999	2000	2001 (provisional)
Area ('000 hectares)	417	473	534	537	402	451
Yield (tonnes/hectares)	2.96	3.23	2.94	3.23	2.81	2.57
Volume of harvested production	1 234	1 527	1 566	1 737	1 157	1 159
of which:						
Production not on set-aside land:						
Area ('000 hectares)	417	445	506	417	332	404
Yield (tonnes/hectares) (a)	2.97	3.24	2.95	3.24	2.90	2.57
Production (a)	1 234	1 444	1 493	1 354	965	1 038
Production on set-aside land:						
Area ('000 hectares)	..	28	27	120	70	48
Yield (tonnes/hectares)	..	3.00	2.67	3.20	2.80	2.53
Production	..	83	73	383	192	121
Value of production (£ million)	292	406	417	371	246	275
of which: sales	262	227	259	202	155	167
subsidies (b) (c)	..	167	155	175	110	103
change in stocks	..	13	3	- 6	- 19	4
Imports from: the EU	128	274	277	208	270	307
the rest of the world	60	3	49	115	18	104
Exports to: the EU	138	162	230	126	50	17
the rest of the world	16	24	46	149	-	-
Total new supply	1 268	1 618	1 616	1 785	1 395	1 553
Production as % of total new supply for use in UK	97%	94%	97%	97%	83%	75%

source: DEFRA Statistics website, www.defra.gov.uk/esg

(a) These figures are on the basis of a standard (9%) moisture content.

(b) Under the Arable Area Payments Scheme (AAPS) until 1999 payments were made to oilseed rape producers in two instalments: an advanced payment in the autumn of the year of harvest and the balance in the following spring. However for the purposes of these accounts all payments have been included under the year of harvest. From 2000, only one payment will be made, in the year of harvest.

(c) In 2000, an area of GM contaminated crop was destroyed. The subsidies valuation includes both the subsidy payment for this area and the compensation payments made.

TABLE 5.6 Linseed

Enquiries: Dave Fernall on 01904 455058   email: david.fernall@defra.gsi.gov.uk

Thousand tonnes (unless otherwise specified)   *Calendar years*

	Average of 1990-92	1997	1998	1999	2000	2001 (provisional)
Area ('000 hectares)	90	76	101	213	74	31
Yield (tonnes/hectare)	1.73	1.40	1.41	1.42	0.58	1.23
Volume of harvested production	150	106	143	302	43	39
of which:						
Production not on set-aside land:						
Area ('000 hectares)	90	73	99	209	72	31
Yield (tonnes/hectares) (a)	1.73	1.39	1.41	1.42	0.56	1.23
Production (a)	150	102	140	297	40	38
Production on set-aside land:						
Area ('000 hectares)	..	3	2	3	2	-
Yield (tonnes/hectares)	..	1.65	1.57	1.55	1.30	1.25
Production	..	5	3	5	3	1
Value of production (£ million)	46	52	68	132	34	16
of which: sales	15	14	20	29	8	6
subsidies (b)	30	37	48	102	29	10
change in stocks	1	-	1	2	- 3	-
Imports from: the EU	7	-	1	2	4	2
the rest of the world	1	52	37	1	3	24
Exports to: the EU	51	30	39	100	63	66
the rest of the world	-	1	1	6	1	-
Total new supply	107	127	141	199	- 14	- 2
Production as % of total new supply for use in UK	137%	83%	101%	152%	-303%	-2567%

source: DEFRA Statistics website, www.defra.gov.uk/esg

(a) These figures are based on a standard (9%) moisture content.

(b) Includes Arable Area Payments but excludes set-aside payments.

TABLE 5.7 Sugar beet and sugar

Enquiries: Dave Fernall on 01904 455058   email: david.fernall@defra.gsi.gov.uk

Thousand tonnes (unless otherwise specified)

Calendar years

	Average of 1990-92	1997	1998	1999	2000	2001 (provisional)
Sugar beet (a)						
Area ('000 ha)	196	196	189	183	173	177
Yield (adjusted tonnes/hectares)	45.55	56.55	53.00	57.95	52.48	46.11
Volume of harvested production (a)	8 917	11 084	10 002	10 584	9 079	8 180
Average market price (£/adjusted tonne)(b)	36	30	30	26	28	31
Value of production (£ million)	324	329	298	280	252	255
Sugar content %	17.23	17.17	17.34	17.16	17.10	17.15
Sugar ('000 tonnes refined basis)						
Production (c)	1 312	1 592	1 439	1 548	1 325	1 200
Imports from: the EU	143	125	156	117	143	116
the rest of the world	1 181	1 133	1 178	1 137	1 148	1 194
Exports to: the EU	73	73	84	83	90	67
the rest of the world	229	511	687	534	608	541
Total new supply	2 334	2 267	2 002	2 185	1 919	1 903
Production as % of total new supply for use in UK	56%	70%	72%	71%	69%	63%

source: DEFRA Statistics website, www.defra.gov.uk/esg

(a) From 1991 onwards yield, production and prices for sugar beet have been re-based to "adjusted tonnes" at standard 16% sugar content.

(b) Average price for all sugar beet, including transport allowance and bonuses.

(c) Sugar coming out of the factory in the early part of the new year is regarded as being part of the previous calendar year's production.

TABLE 5.8 Potatoes

Enquiries: Adrian Roberts on 01904 455074   email: adrian.roberts@defra.gsi.gov.uk

Thousand tonnes (unless otherwise specified)   *Calendar years*

	Average of 1990-92	1997	1998	1999	2000	2001 (provisional)
Production						
Area ('000 hectares)	178.4	165.9	164.1	177.6	166.0	165.9
of which: early	16.3	17.5	17.8	13.8	12.2	7.5
maincrop	162.1	148.4	146.3	163.8	153.8	158.4
Yield (tonnes/hectare):						
early	24.9	22.0	18.9	23.3	22.6	23.2
maincrop	40.1	45.4	41.6	41.6	41.5	40.1
overall	38.7	43.0	39.1	40.1	40.1	39.4
Volume of harvested production	6 909	7 128	6 422	7 131	6 652	6 528
of which: early	404	386	336	322	276	175
maincrop	6 505	6 742	6 086	6 809	6 375	6 354
End year stocks	3 571	3 696	3 349	3 706	3 062	3 205
Value of production (£million)	545	390	630	750	454	600
of which: sales	505	387	660	678	499	573
on farm seed use	21	9	12	30	9	12
change in stocks	18	- 7	- 42	43	- 54	15
Prices						
Average price (£/tonne) paid to registered						
producers for: early potatoes (a)	103	74	152	75	132	184
maincrop potatoes (a)	88	63	119	119	80	102
all potatoes (a)(b)	89	66	122	119	83	105
Supply and use						
Total production	6 909	7 128	6 422	7 131	6 652	6 528
Supplies from the Channel Islands	45	58	38	44	43	47
Imports	934	1 017	1 194	1 105	1 185	1 530
of which:						
early from:						
the EU	83	77	77	65	65	44
the rest of the world	162	89	124	128	81	95
maincrop from:						
the EU	64	79	197	69	167	462
the rest of the world	18	2	5	7	8	5
processed (raw equivalent) from:						
the EU	533	736	758	772	818	862
the rest of the world	35	16	16	44	17	23
seed from:						
the EU	38	19	17	19	30	39
the rest of the world	-	-	-	-	-	-
Exports	251	363	375	339	370	319
of which:						
raw to:						
the EU	69	148	175	156	154	108
the rest of the world	50	9	8	3	8	2
processed (raw equivalent) to:						
the EU	61	73	84	82	93	107
the rest of the world	3	46	25	20	35	21
seed to:						
the EU	31	35	49	31	32	73
the rest of the world	37	53	34	46	48	9
Total new supply	7 637	7 840	7 279	7 941	7 510	7 786
Change in stocks	263	- 98	- 347	358	- 645	143

TABLE 5.8 *cont.*

Thousand tonnes (unless otherwise specified)   *Calendar years*

	Average of 1990-92	1997	1998	1999	2000	2001 (provisional)
Total domestic uses	7 374	7 938	7 626	7 584	8 155	7 643
of which: used for human consumption	5 911	6 279	5 997	6 210	6 523	6 429
seed for home crops (including seed imports)	545	449	437	446	452	381
support buying	184	-	-	-	-	-
chats, waste and retained stockfeed	735	1 210	1 192	928	1 180	833
Production as % of total new supply for use in the UK	90%	91%	88%	90%	89%	84%

source: DEFRA Statistics website, www.defra.gov.uk/esg

(Crop Years: June-May)

'000 tonnes (unless otherwise specified)

	1996/7	1997/98	1998/99	1999/00	2000/01
Production					
Volume of harvested production	7 228	7 128	6 422	7 131	6 652
Value of production (£ million)	406	476	853	450	624
of which: sales	389	463	829	438	603
on farm seed use	22	9	16	24	7
change in stocks	- 5	4	8	- 13	14
Prices					
Average realised return (£/tonne) (c)	66	81	159	74	116

source: DEFRA Statistics website, www.defra.gov.uk/esg

(a) Includes a price for sacks where appropriate.

(b) Takes account of support buying and seed sales.

(c) Takes account of support buying, seed sales and sacks.

TABLE 5.9 Peas and Beans for Stockfeed

Enquiries: Ann Reed on 01904 455059   email: ann.reed@defra.gsi.gov.uk

Thousand tonnes (unless otherwise specified)   *Calendar years*

	Average of 1990-92	1997	1998	1999	2000	2001 (provisional)
Peas for harvesting dry (a)						
Area ('000 hectares)	61	78	82	71	67	79
Yield (tonnes/hectare)	3.71	3.79	3.17	4.00	3.69	3.54
Volume of harvested production (a)	224	297	259	285	247	280
Value of production (£ million)	39	56	47	46	39	45
of which: sales	39	29	19	22	20	25
subsidies (b)	-	28	28	24	19	20
Field beans (mainly for stockfeed)						
Area ('000 hectares)	133	99	111	113	124	169
Yield (tonnes/hectare)	3.37	3.80	3.41	3.50	3.90	3.50
Volume of harvested production (a)	448	378	378	395	485	590
Value of production (£ million)	76	72	66	69	74	96
of which: sales	76	37	28	30	39	53
subsidies (b)	-	36	38	38	35	43

source: DEFRA Statistics website, www.defra.gov.uk/esg

(a) The figures presented here cover only that part of the crop which is assumed to be used for stockfeed (80% of total production); the remainder is included in Horticulture: vegetables, Table 5.10.

(b) Includes Arable Area Payments but excludes set-aside payments.

2001

Horticulture

Horticulture

(Tables 5.10 – 5.12)

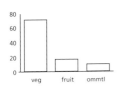

% of total area 2001

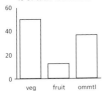

% of total value 2001

13 The total area devoted to horticulture as reported in the 2001 June Agricultural Census (table 3.2) was 172,734 hectares, compared with 172,310 hectares in 2000.

14 The publication 'Basic Horticultural Statistics' expands on the details of all crops shown in this horticultural section and also provides statistics for hops. Copies can be obtained from Mrs. Lesly Lawton, DEFRA, Statistics (Commodities and Food), Hort & Poultry Branch, Room 230, Foss House, King's Pool, 1-2 Peasholme Green, York, YO1 7PX (tel. 01904 455072) or at www.defra.gov.uk.

Field vegetables grown in the open

(Table 5.10)

15 The area of field vegetables rose by 6.0 per cent in 2001, reversing the trend of the last two years. The value of production increased by 16 per cent. Although there was a decrease of 23 per cent in the value of cauliflowers, the value of brassicas as a whole increased by 4.6 per cent. The value of roots and onions increased by 28 per cent with the value of carrots also rising, by 28 per cent. Legumes decreased in value by 3.3 per cent. The value of mushrooms was unchanged. Excessive rainfall in all areas during the autumn and winter of 2000 continued into 2001 which led to difficult harvesting conditions and ultimately a shortage of some vegetables.

Protected salad crops

(Table 5.10)

16 The area of protected vegetables fell by 6.9 per cent continuing the downward trend of the last few years. The value of production rose slightly, with an increase of 0.8 per cent. Crops began well but poor weather during the summer and autumn of 2001 reduced production. The value of tomatoes fell by 9.0 per cent which was mainly due to a drop in production combined with poor demand and increased levels of disease.

Orchard fruit

(Table 5.11)

17 Orchard fruit area was unchanged in 2001. The value of production for orchard fruit rose by 17.6 per cent due in part to good demand and prices for dessert apples. Culinary apples showed a slight increase in value of 1.0 per cent. The value of production of pears rose by 40 per cent.

Soft fruit

(Table 5.11)

18 Soft fruit area was unchanged in 2001, as was the overall value of production. The value of production for strawberries fell by 1.8 per cent due mainly to competition from imports and poor yields. The value of production for raspberries rose by 19.6 per cent due to increased quality and fruit size.

Flowers in the open and bulbs (open and forced)

(Table 5.12)

19 Value of production of the relatively small flowers and bulbs sector increased by 1.4 per cent in 2001. An extended narcissus season increased the value of the cut flower crop, despite some labour shortages, with forced lilies and irises selling well. Some outdoor flowers also saw higher returns, although narcissus bulb prices were below those of 2000.

Hardy ornamental nursery stock
(Table 5.12)

[20] The value of production increased by 5.6 per cent. Although prices of field -grown nursery stock remained flat, the landscape sector remained very competitive. Small price rises were seen in some lines of container-grown plants.

Protected ornamentals
(Table 5.12)

[21] The value for protected ornamentals rose by 5.3 per cent with sales of nursery stock variable due to the poor weather. Increases in the value of bedding plants were seen as a result of increased demand from some retail sectors of the market, more 'added value' plants and an increased valuation for some pack material.

TABLE 5.10 Horticulture: vegetables

Enquiries: Lesly Lawton on 01904 455072   email: lesly.lawton@defra.gsi.gov.uk

Thousand tonnes (unless otherwise specified)   *Calendar years*

	Average of 1990-92	1997	1998	1999	2000	2001 (provisional)
Production						
Area ('000 hectares):	185.3	152.7	155.9	149.1	137.0	145.1
of which: grown in the open (a)(b)	182.7	151.3	154.6	147.9	135.8	144.0
protected (c)	2.7	1.4	1.3	1.2	1.2	1.1
Value of production (£million):	979	962	989	962	877	970
grown in the open	636	637	664	645	568	659
protected	343	324	325	318	308	311
of which: subsidies (d)	..	7	7	6	5	5
Selected crops:						
cabbages	64	56	59	55	49	63
carrots	83	67	88	94	74	95
cauliflowers	70	46	41	36	42	33
lettuces	126	120	95	103	82	108
mushrooms	158	169	174	170	150	150
peas	60	59	55	57	59	56
tomatoes	79	62	64	67	78	71
Prices						
Farm gate price (£/tonne)						
Selected crops:						
cauliflowers	219.6	236.8	216.3	211.3	270.0	272.1
tomatoes	605.7	542.9	591.3	571.6	687.0	649.3
Supply and use (e)						
Total production	3 131	2 938	2 864	2 954	2 879	2 729
Supplies from the Channel Islands	26	19	16	16	15	15
Imports from: the EU	741	1 131	1 085	1 086	1 092	1 252
the rest of the world	241	117	149	163	156	157
Exports to: the EU	47	87	71	89	97	112
the rest of the world	4	7	5	3	2	3
Total new supply	4088	4 126	4 056	4 140	4 060	4 080
Production as % of total new supply for use in the UK	77%	71%	71%	71%	71%	67%

source: DEFRA Statistics website, www.defra.gov.uk/esg

(a) Includes peas harvested dry for human consumption.

(b) Areas relate to field areas multiplied by the number of crops in the year and hence differ from those shown in table 3.2

(c) Excludes mushrooms area from 1992.

(d) Arable Area Payments for peas harvested dry.

(e) Trade figures relate to fresh produce where distinguishable.

TABLE 5.11 Horticulture: fruit

Enquiries: Lesly Lawton on 01904 455072   email: lesly.lawton@defra.gsi.gov.uk

Thousand tonnes (unless otherwise specified)   *Calendar years*

	Average of 1990-92	1997	1998	1999	2000	2001 (provisional)
Production						
Area ('000 hectares):	45.5	38.6	35.9	34.2	33.4	33.4
of which: orchard fruit (a)	31.7	27.7	26.7	25.3	24.5	24.5
soft fruit (b)	13.9	10.8	9.2	8.9	8.9	8.9
End year stocks (c)	..	48.9	93.3	73.5	79.2	92.8
Value of production (£million) (e):	275	199	259	257	228	243
of which: orchard fruit (d)	149	80	126	106	83	97
soft fruit	125	111	125	139	133	133
of which: sales	274	228	234	265	226	238
change in stocks (c)	1	- 30	24	- 8	2	6
Selected crops:						
dessert apples	75	50	47	59	36	36
culinary apples	36	29	29	28	23	23
pears	17	15	11	10	7	10
raspberries	27	24	35	37	26	31
strawberries	68	69	75	87	81	80
Prices						
Farm gate price (£/tonne)						
Selected crops:						
dessert apples	458.7	525.7	480.3	436.8	357.8	374.5
culinary apples	194.8	322.0	341.4	248.9	215.3	216.0
pears	502.6	441.9	405.1	426.4	278.3	321.6
Supply and use (f)						
Total production	503	291	277	345	304	315
Supplies from the Channel Islands	..	19	16	16	15	15
Imports from: the EU	1 072	1 196	1 362	1 160	1 240	1 218
the rest of the world	1 156	1 344	1 405	1 515	1 495	1 568
Exports to: the EU	73	78	67	73	59	66
the rest of the world	4	3	7	1	-	1
Total new supply	2 655	2 769	2 988	2 962	2 994	3 049
Net increase in stocks	- 1	- 56	44	- 20	6	14
Total domestic uses	2 657	2 826	2 943	2 981	2 988	3 036
Production as % of total new supply for use in the UK	19%	11%	9%	12%	10%	10%

source: DEFRA Statistics website, www.defra.gov.uk/esg

(a) Includes field area of commercial orchards only, and may therefore differ from the area in table 3.2, which also includes non-commercial orchards.

(b) Excludes area of wine grapes and may therefore differ from the area in table 3.2.

(c) Stocks relate to apples and pears.

(d) Excludes EC grubbing up grant.

(e) Includes glasshouse fruit.

(f) Trade figures relate to fresh produce where distinguishable.

TABLE 5.12 Horticulture: ornamentals

Enquiries: Lisa Szydlowska 01904 455070   email: lisa.szydlowska@defra.gsi.gov.uk

Thousand tonnes (unless otherwise specified)   *Calendar years*

	Average of 1990-92	1997	1998	1999	2000	2001 (provisional)
Production						
Area ('000 hectares) (a)	19	20	19	20	20	20
Value of production (£million)	519	671	650	715	672	708
of which: flowers and bulbs in the open (b)	43	47	38	34	31	31
hardy ornamental nursery stock	263	353	352	400	374	395
protected crops	215	271	260	280	268	282
Prices			not available			
Supply and use			Imports/exports of ornamentals available in "Basic Horticultural Statistics"			

source: DEFRA Statistics website, www.defra.gov.uk/esg

(a) Areas relate to field areas multiplied by the number of crops in the year and hence differ from those shown in table 3.2.

(b) Including forced flower bulbs.

Livestock

Foot and mouth disease **22** The first confirmed case of foot and mouth disease in the UK was on 20 February 2001. There were 2,030 confirmed cases during the year with the last case confirmed on 30 September 2001. There were 1,730 cases in England, 183 in Scotland, 113 in Wales and 4 in Northern Ireland. Over the year 10,075 premises had animals slaughtered for disease control purposes.

23 The disease peaked during March and April, and then tailed off from May onwards. The chart below shows the number of cases per day.

Chart 5.1 UK daily cases of foot and mouth disease

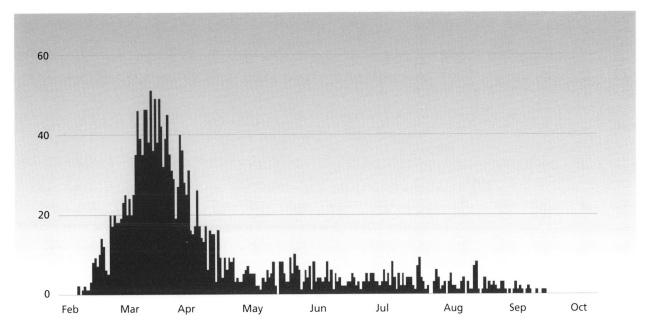

24 The disease was present in some regions more than others with the most affected counties being Dumfries and Galloway, Cumbria, Northumberland, North Yorkshire, Durham, Lancashire, Powys, Gloucestershire and Devon.

25 The Livestock Welfare Disposal Scheme was opened on 22 March 2001 to deal with severe welfare problems arising from the foot and mouth movement restrictions that could not be dealt with by any other means.

26 The total number of animals slaughtered for disease control purposes was 4,082,000. The total number of animals slaughtered for welfare reasons for the year 2001 was 2,046,000. A further 526,000 were slaughtered under the Light Lambs Scheme. The figures are broken down as follows with a comparison with the populations at June 2000.

Animal	Numbers slaughtered for disease control	Numbers slaughtered for welfare reasons	Total numbers as at June 2000
Cattle	592,000	169,000	11,135,000
Sheep	3,343,000	1,585,000 (a)	42,264,000
Pigs	142,000	287,000	6,482,000
Other	5,000	5,000	

(a) in addition 526,000 lambs were slaughtered under the Light Lambs Scheme

27 Direct compensation payments for foot and mouth disease totalled £991 million and the compensation paid through the Livestock Welfare Disposal Scheme came to £224 million.

28 Throughout the crisis the export of livestock and livestock products was banned. Export of pigmeat from provisionally free areas was allowed to be resumed at the end of October 2001. All remaining trade restrictions on the export of meat, animal products and livestock to Europe were lifted on 7 February 2002 by the Standing Vetinary Committee of the European Comission.

29 The UK was declared disease free on 14 January 2002.

Cattle and calves: beef and veal

(Table 5.13)

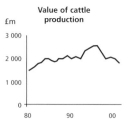

30 The value of production of cattle and calves fell by 9.5 per cent in 2001 to £1,809 million, the lowest for 19 years, due primarily to a 10 per cent fall in the value of home-fed production of beef and veal, a decrease in unfinished production (work in progress on animals to be slaughtered) and a 5.9 per cent fall in subsidy and other payments to beef producers. The latter was mainly a fall in receipts arising from the closure of the Over Thirty Month Scheme (OTMS) for five months during the year and the replacement of the Hill Livestock Compensatory Allowance with land area-based schemes (which are not included in this table as they are not direct subsidy payments).

31 Clean cattle marketings fell by 11 per cent in 2001 as a result of the outbreak of foot and mouth disease. Although dressed carcase weights increased slightly, the fall in marketings was reflected in a fall of 8.6 per cent in home-fed production to 645 thousand tonnes.

32 The amount of beef available for domestic use, however, fell by only 2.6 per cent, to 889 thousand tonnes, due to increased imports which largely offset the shortfall in production.

33 Measures of marketings, production and value exclude all cattle removed from the food chain by the OTMS, the Selective Cull and the Calf Processing Aid Scheme

2001

(CPAS, which ran from 22 April 1996 until 31 July 1999). These schemes were introduced following the beef crisis in March 1996. Payments to producers for the OTMS and CPAS are included as subsidies in the value of production. Payments under the Selective Cull are not included as the payments are for the replacement of capital assets.

34 Cattle slaughtered due to foot and mouth disease (including the preventative operations intended to circumscribe the outbreaks) and under the Welfare Disposal Scheme are also not included in marketings, production and value as these animals were removed from the food chain. Also foot and mouth compensation payments are not included in the value of production as these have been treated as payments for the loss of capital assets.

35 Gross Indigenous Production (GIP) is a measure of animal production commonly used in other EU states and is therefore useful for making international comparisons. It is measured as total slaughterings plus all live exports minus all live imports (breeding and non-breeding). GIP differs from home-fed production in that exports and imports of breeding animals are included in its calculation and, for other imported animals, includes only the weight added since their arrival in the country. Both measures include the export weight (dressed carcase weight equivalent) of animals intended for slaughter abroad.

36 The value of production of sheep and lambs fell by 35 per cent to £625 million in 2001, the lowest for 19 years, owing primarily to a 32 per cent fall in the value of home-fed production and a 43 per cent fall in subsidy payments. Higher average EU market prices resulted in a lower payment rate for Sheep Annual Premium and the Hill Livestock Compensatory Allowance was replaced by land area-based schemes (which are not included in this table as they are not direct subsidy payments).

Sheep and lambs: mutton and lamb

(Table 5.14)

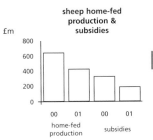

sheep home-fed production & subsidies

37 Clean sheep marketings fell by 34 per cent in 2001, due primarily to the outbreak of foot and mouth disease. Sheepmeat production fell by a similar margin of 32 per cent, to 265 thousand tonnes, as the fall in marketings was only slightly offset by the highest average carcase weights for clean sheep seen in recent years.

38 However, the amount of sheepmeat available for domestic use fell by 15 per cent to 335 thousand tonnes. The large fall in production was partially compensated for by the fall in exports which resulted from the export ban imposed at the start of the outbreak of foot and mouth disease.

39 Sheep slaughtered due to foot and mouth disease (including the preventative operations intended to circumscribe the outbreak) and under the Welfare Disposal Scheme are not included in marketings, production and value as these animals were removed from the food chain. Also foot and mouth compensation payments are not included in the value of production as these have been treated as payments for the loss of capital assets. However, the 'light lambs' scheme, which operated in the autumn, has been included as a subsidy in the output value of production.

40 Gross Indigenous Production (GIP) is a measure of animal production commonly used in other EU states and is therefore useful for making international comparisons. See paragraph 35 for further details.

Pigs and pigmeat
(Table 5.15)

Value of pig production

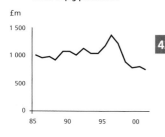

£m

41 The value of production of pigs fell by 5.4 per cent in 2001 to £751 million, nearly half the peak value of £1,374 million in 1996. The value of home-fed production of pigmeat fell by 9.9 per cent but this was partly offset by a £41 million increase in the value of unfinished production (work in progress on pigs to be slaughtered).

42 Marketings of clean pigs fell by 14 per cent, primarily due to the contraction of the breeding herd in the previous year as a result of poor market returns. The outbreaks of foot and mouth disease in 2001 and Classical Swine Fever in the autumn of 2000 also had an effect. Marketings of sows and boars also fell substantially, by 43 per cent, as the export ban put in place at the start of the outbreak of foot and mouth disease removed the main market for sow meat. Although average carcase weights continued to increase, home-fed production of pigmeat fell by 13 per cent to 777 thousand tonnes.

43 This decrease was reflected in the production of pork, which fell by 16 per cent, to 610 thousand tonnes. However, the amount available for domestic use rose slightly by 0.6 per cent to 802 thousand tonnes, as the fall in production was compensated for by the meat available for use in the United Kingdom as a result of the export ban imposed at the start of the outbreak of foot and mouth disease.

44 Home-cured production of bacon fell by 5.8 per cent, to 197 thousand tonnes. However, the amount available for domestic use fell by 2.4 per cent to 457 thousand tonnes as the fall in production was partly offset by the reduction in exports as a result of the export ban.

45 Pigs slaughtered due to foot and mouth disease or Classical Swine Fever (including the preventative operations intended to circumscribe the outbreak) and under the welfare disposal schemes are not included in marketings, production and value as these animals were removed from the food chain. Also foot and mouth disease compensation payments are not included in the value of production as these have been treated as payments for the loss of capital assets.

46 Gross Indigenous Production (GIP) is a measure of animal production commonly used in other EU states and is therefore useful for making international comparisons. See paragraph 35 for further details.

Poultry and poultrymeat
(Table 5.16)

Poultry production
'000 tonnes

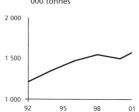

47 The volume of poultrymeat production rose by 3.4 per cent in 2001 with overall slaughterings rising by 2.7 per cent. The value of production in 2001 increased by 1.0 per cent to £1,317 million. Poultrymeat prices fell during 2001, with turkey meat falling by 5.3 per cent to 122.7 pence per kilogramme. Imports fell by 3.4 per cent, the first time they have fallen since 1988. Exports rose by 1.8 per cent.

TABLE 5.13 Cattle and calves; beef and veal

Enquiries: Keith Seabridge on 01904 455091   email: keith.seabridge@defra.gsi.gov.uk.

Calendar years

	Average of 1990-92	1997	1998 (a)	1999	2000	2001 (provisional)
Population						
Total cattle and calves ('000 head at June)	12 040	11 633	11 519	11 423	11 133	10 600
of which: dairy cows	2 767	2 478	2 439	2 440	2 336	2 251
beef cows	1 688	1 862	1 947	1 924	1 842	1 708
dairy heifers in-calf	537	599	563	549	532	502
beef heifers in-calf	219	249	225	214	186	199
other	6 829	6 444	6 345	6 296	6 238	5 940
Production						
Total home-fed marketings ('000 head) (b)	3 869	2 293	2 312	2 296	2 422	2 144
of which: steers, heifers and young bulls	2 749	2 269	2 276	2 216	2 265	2 049
calves	428	20	32	75	153	92
cows and adult bulls	693	5	4	4	4	3
Average dressed carcase weights (dcw) (kgs) (b) (c):						
steers, heifers and young bulls	288.1	306.8	306.6	304.6	308.9	313.2
calves	58.0	49.0	35.3	31.6	27.5	27.5
cows and adult bulls	281.5	264.2	251.1	273.6	249.2	254.1
Production ('000 tonnes, dcw) (b):						
Home-fed production	1 001	698	699	679	706	645
Gross indigenous production	990	692	698	676	702	639
Value of production (£ million)	1 998	2 276	1 982	2 048	2 000	1 809
of which: Value of home-fed production (£ million) (b)	1 880	1 194	1 055	1 094	1 114	1 000
Subsidies (£ million) (d)	192	1 116	923	902	899	847
Change in work in progress (£ million) (e)	- 47	- 28	6	54	- 12	- 36
Less imported livestock (£ million)	28	5	3	2	2	1
plus breeding animals exported (£ million)	1	..	..	..	..	..
Prices						
Store cattle (£ per head) (f):						
1st quality Hereford/cross bull calves (g)	131.1	147.0	107.9	88.2	79.5	..
1st quality beef/cross yearling steers (h)	404.6	427.0	369.0	382.0	400.0	..
Finished cattle (p per kg liveweight): All clean cattle	107.6	96.9	86.1	92.1	89.7	..
Over Thirty Month, Selective Cull and Calf Processing Aid Schemes (i)						
Over Thirty Month Scheme:						
Clean cattle throughput ('000 head)	..	72	71	72	62	55
Cull cattle throughput ('000 head)	..	779	826	898	910	564
Receipts (£ million)	..	362	239	266	260	157
Selective Cull scheme:						
Throughput ('000 head)	..	57	19	-	-	-
Receipts (£ million)	..	78	43	-	-	-
Calf Processing Aid Scheme:						
Throughput ('000 head)	..	596	671	307	..	..
Receipts (£ million)	..	54	52	20	..	..
Supply and use ('000 tonnes, dcw) (j)						
Home-fed production (b)	1 001	698	699	679	706	645
Imports from: the EU (k)	162	141	92	125	133	175
the rest of the world	40	75	60	59	64	78
Exports to: the EU (l)	129	13	9	9	11	9
the rest of the world	26	1	-	-	-	-
Total new supply	1 048	901	842	853	892	889
Increase in stocks	58	37	- 16	- 83	- 21	-
Total domestic uses	990	865	858	936	913	889

TABLE 5.13 *cont.*

Calendar years

	Average of 1990-92	1997	1998 (a)	1999	2000	2001 (provisional)
Home-fed production as % of total new supply for use in UK	96%	77%	83%	80%	79%	73%
Closing stocks	200	160	144	61	40	40

source: DEFRA Statistics website, www.defra.gov.uk/esg

(a) For comparability with other years, the figures have been adjusted from a 53-week to a 52-week basis where appropriate.

(b) Excludes cattle slaughtered under the Over Thirty Month Scheme and Selective Cull and calves slaughtered under the Calf Processing Aid Scheme. Also excludes cattle slaughtered under foot and mouth disease control measures and Livestock Welfare Disposal Scheme.

(c) Average dressed carcase weight of animals fed and slaughtered in the UK.

(d) Comprising variable premium, calf subsidy, hill livestock compensatory allowances, suckler cow premium, beef special premium, deseasonalisation premium, extensification payments and slaughter premium. Includes payments made under the Over Thirty Month Scheme and the Calf Processing Aid Scheme.

(e) A valuation of the change in work in progress of animals to be slaughtered.

(f) Average prices at representative markets in England and Wales.

(g) Category change January 1988: Formerly 1st quality Hereford/Friesian bull calves.

(h) Category change January 1988: Formerly 1st quality yearling steers beef/dairy cross. Now consists of Hereford/cross, Charolais/cross, Limousin/cross, Simmental/cross, Belgian blue/cross, other continental/cross, other beef/dairy cross, other beef/beef cross.

(i) Cattle slaughtered under these schemes are not included within the volume of production. Receipts for the Over Thirty Month Scheme and the Calf Processing Aid Scheme are included as subsidies. Selective Cull payments are not included in the income account.

(j) Does not include meat offals or trade in preserved or manufactured meat products. Boneless meat has been converted to bone-in weights.

(k) Includes meat from finished animals imported from the Irish Republic.

(l) Adjusted, as necessary, for unrecorded trade in live animals.

TABLE 5.14 Sheep and lambs; mutton and lamb

Enquiries: Keith Seabridge on 01904 455091   email: keith.seabridge@defra.gsi.gov.uk.

Calendar years

	Average of 1990-92	1997	1998 (a)	1999	2000	2001 (provisional)
Population						
Total sheep and lambs ('000 head at June)	44 392	42 823	44 471	44 656	42 261	36 697
of which: breeding flock	20 728	20 696	21 260	21 458	20 447	17 911
lambs under 1 year old	22 400	21 032	22 138	22 092	20 855	17 759
others	1 264	1 095	1 073	1 106	959	1 027
Production						
(excluding clip wool)						
Total home-fed marketings ('000 head) (b)	21 737	18 123	20 215	21 342	19 939	13 213
of which: clean sheep and lambs	19 680	16 087	18 132	18 950	17 416	11 448
ewes and rams	2 057	2 036	2 083	2 391	2 523	1 765
Average dressed carcase weights (dcw) (kgs) (b) (c):						
clean sheep and lambs	17.8	18.0	17.8	17.6	18.2	18.7
ewes and rams	26.9	29.1	29.7	28.3	28.5	28.3
Production ('000 tonnes, dcw) (b):						
home-fed production	406	351	385	403	389	265
gross indigenous production	406	351	385	403	389	265
Value of production (£ million)	1 104	1 194	1 130	1 025	960	625
of which: value of home-fed production (£ million) (b)	610	797	644	613	651	442
subsidies (£ million) (d)	505	354	479	432	330	187
change in work in progress (£ million) (e)	- 8	47	11	- 15	- 15	- 2
Less imported livestock (£ million)	4	5	4	5	7	1
plus breeding animals exported (£ million)	-	-	-	-	-	-
Prices						
Store sheep (£ per head):						
1st quality lambs, hoggets and tegs (f)	35.7	53.4	31.3	28.6	34.5	..
Finished sheep (p per kg estimated dcw) (g):						
Great Britain	168.3	239.0	192.5	180.3	196.4	..
Northern Ireland	174.2	228.2	179.1	165.7	182.7	..
Supplies ('000 tonnes, dcw) (h)						
Home-fed production (b)	406	351	385	403	389	265
Imports from: the EU (i)	5	22	18	17	17	14
the rest of the world	130	129	124	121	117	102
Exports to: the EU (j)	121	139	146	153	132	46
the rest of the world	2	2	1	1	1	-
Total new supply	418	362	380	386	390	334
Increase in stocks	- 2	2	-	- 1	- 5	- 1
Total domestic uses	419	360	381	387	395	335
Home-fed production as % of total new supply for use in UK	98%	97%	101%	104%	100%	79%
Closing stocks	18	15	15	14	9	8

source: DEFRA Statistics website, www.defra.gov.uk/esg

(a) For comparability with other years, the figures have been adjusted from a 53-week to a 52-week basis where appropriate.

(b) Excludes sheep and lambs slaughtered under foot and mouth disease control measures and livestock welfare disposal scheme (including 'light lambs' scheme).

(c) Average dressed carcase weight of animals fed and slaughtered in the UK.

(d) Comprising variable premium, hill livestock compensatory allowances, sheep annual premium and 'light lambs' welfare disposal scheme.

(e) A valuation of the change in work in progress of animals to be slaughtered.

(f) Average prices at representative markets in England and Wales, excluding prices at autumn hill sheep sales.

(g) Unweighted average of weekly prices at representative markets as reported to the European Commission.

(h) Does not include meat offals or trade in preserved or manufactured meat products. Boneless meat has been converted to bone-in weights.

(i) Includes meat from finished animals imported from the Irish Republic.

(j) Adjusted, as necessary, for unrecorded trade in live animals.

TABLE 5.15 Pigs and pigmeat

Enquiries: Keith Seabridge on 01904 455091   email: keith.seabridge@defra.gsi.gov.uk.

Calendar years

	Average of 1990-92	1997	1998 (a)	1999	2000	2001 (provisional)
Population						
Total pigs ('000 head at June)	7 650	8 072	8 146	7 284	6 482	5 845
of which: sows in pig and other sows for breeding	681	683	675	603	537	527
gilts in pig	110	116	103	85	73	71
other	6 859	7 272	7 368	6 595	5 872	5 247
Production						
Total home-fed marketings ('000 head) (b)	14 745	15 479	16 058	14 691	12 376	10 571
of which: clean pigs	14 377	15 097	15 640	14 313	12 054	10 388
sows and boars	368	381	418	378	322	182
Average dressed carcase weights (dcw) (kgs) (b) (c):						
clean pigs	65.4	68.9	69.1	69.1	70.7	72.1
sows and boars	145.1	141.7	142.3	145.3	148.4	156.0
Production ('000 tonnes, dcw) (b):						
home-fed production	993	1 091	1 135	1 042	899	777
gross indigenous production	993	1 090	1 135	1 043	900	777
Value of production (£ million)	1 082	1 204	888	788	794	751
of which: value of home-fed production (£ million) (b)	1 071	1 186	890	795	821	740
change in work in progress (£ million) (d)	3	10	- 8	- 11	- 31	10
Less imported livestock (£ million)	..	..	..	..	..	..
plus breeding animals exported (£ million)	8	8	5	4	4	-
Prices						
Clean pigs (p per kg deadweight)	109.8	110.8	80.6	78.6	94.4	97.7
Supplies of pork ('000 tonnes, dcw) (e) (f)						
Home-fed production (b)	792	888	931	831	725	610
Imports from: the EU (g)	81	175	187	231	269	251
the rest of the world	1	2	3	3	5	3
Exports to: the EU (h)	105	218	258	201	175	53
the rest of the world	2	30	35	34	33	4
Total new supply	768	817	829	831	790	807
Increase in stocks	-	2	2	- 3	- 7	5
Total domestic uses	768	815	827	834	798	802
Home-fed production as % of total new supply for use in UK	103%	109%	112%	100%	92%	76%
Closing stocks	11	16	18	15	8	13
Supplies of bacon and ham						
('000 tonnes, product weight) (e)						
Home-cured production	191	239	236	233	209	197
Imports from: the EU	249	240	231	230	268	268
the rest of the world	-	-	-	-	-	-
Exports to: the EU	5	8	8	6	9	5
the rest of the world	-	-	-	-	1	-
Total new supply	435	471	459	457	468	460
Increase in stocks	- 2	2	- 1	2	-	3
Total domestic uses	437	470	460	455	468	457
Home-cured production as % of total new supply for use in UK	44%	51%	51%	51%	45%	43%
Closing stocks	4	4	3	5	4	7

source: DEFRA Statistics website, www.defra.gov.uk/esg

continued

TABLE 5.15 cont.

(a) For comparability with other years, the figures have been adjusted from a 53-week to a 52-week basis where appropriate.

(b) Excludes pigs slaughtered under foot and mouth disease and swine fever control measures and welfare disposal schemes.

(c) Average dressed carcase weight of animals fed and slaughtered in the UK.

(d) A valuation of the change in work in progress of animals to be slaughtered.

(e) Does not include meat offals or trade in preserved or manufactured meat products.

(f) Boneless meat has been converted to bone-in weights.

(g) Includes meat from finished animals imported from the Irish Republic.

(h) Adjusted, as necessary, for unrecorded trade in live animals.

2001

TABLE 5.16 Poultry and poultrymeat

Enquiries: Adrian Roberts on 01904 455074   email: adrian.roberts@defra.gsi.gov.uk

Calendar years

	Average of 1990-92	1997	1998 (a)	1999	2000	2001 (provisional)
Production						
Number ('000 head at June) (b):	117 500	..	152 886	153 590	157 052	167 549
of which: chickens and other table fowls	74 601	..	98 244	101 625	105 688	114 296
birds in the laying flock (c)	33 463	..	29 483	29 258	28 686	29 556
fowls for breeding	7 184	..	10 023	9 401	10 668	11 308
turkeys, ducks & geese (d)	2 253	..	15 136	13 306	12 010	12 389
Slaughterings (millions)(e):	691	850	856	848	843	865
of which: fowls	646	796	804	800	797	818
turkeys	32	36	34	29	27	26
ducks	12	17	17	18	18	20
geese	1	1	1	1	1	1
Production ('000 tonnes carcase weight)(f):	1 186	1 520	1 545	1 525	1 513	1 564
of which: chickens and other table fowls	902	1 130	1 153	1 161	1 164	1 209
boiling fowls (culled hens)	47	56	56	53	51	49
turkeys	208	293	294	267	255	258
ducks	27	38	39	41	40	46
geese	3	3	3	3	3	2
Value of production (£ million):	1 097	1 494	1 365	1 272	1 303	1 317
of which: fowls	772	993	892	839	830	851
change in work in progress in fowls	-	8	- 11	- 21	2	- 4
turkeys, ducks, geese	291	445	429	397	408	400
exports of live poultry	28	45	45	50	60	63
hatching eggs for export	10	14	19	15	13	15
less live poultry imported	3	6	5	5	5	5
less hatching eggs imported	1	6	3	4	5	5
Prices						
Average producer price (p/kg carcase weight) for:						
chickens and other table fowls	83.7	86.1	76.8	71.8	70.8	70.0
boiling fowls (culled hens)	37.4	36.2	11.5	10.3	10.7	9.7
turkeys	120.0	129.1	122.3	118.8	129.6	122.7
ducks	125.6	157.9	161.6	173.8	170.3	165.4
geese	189.2	230.8	211.9	309.8	319.4	257.6
Supply and use of poultrymeat						
('000 tonnes carcase weight) (e)						
Production	1 186	1 520	1 545	1 525	1 513	1 564
Imports from: the EU	157	256	293	318	321	310
the rest of the world	-	20	23	31	34	33
Exports to: the EU	60	134	128	110	116	118
the rest of the world	17	79	69	76	58	59
Total new supply	1 266	1 584	1 664	1 687	1 694	1 730
Change in stocks	5	24	15	- 9	- 13	- 2
Total domestic uses	1 261	1 560	1 649	1 696	1 707	1 733
Production as % of total new supply	94%	96%	93%	90%	89%	90%

source: DEFRA Statistics website, www.defra.gov.uk/esg

(a) For comparability with other years, the figures for 1998 have been adjusted from a 53 week to a 52 week basis.

(b) From 1998 the collection of data for England & Wales was simplified. Figures for 1998 onwards are not directly comparable with years previous to 1998.

(c) Hens and pullets kept mainly for producing eggs for eating.

(d) Pre 1996 data does not include figures for turkeys.

(e) Slaughtering figures include registered and un-registered slaughterhouses.

(f) Excludes offal.

.. Comparable poultry population figures are not available from the 1996 and 1997 June Censuses.

Livestock products

Milk and milk products
(Tables 5.17 and 5.18)

48 The value of production of milk produced for human consumption rose by 18 per cent, to £2,818 million, the highest since 1997. This was primarily due to a £342 million increase in the value of milk sold for processing by dairy companies, which in turn arose mainly from a 13 per cent increase in the average milk price received by farmers in 2001. However, there was also an £11 million increase in the value of dairy products (such as cheese and butter) produced on farm for sale direct to consumers, arising from increased producer prices for these items.

49 In addition, milk producers received £79 million in agrimonetary compensation, paid to holders of quota at March 31 2000, and no superlevy charge arose as milk production in the 2000/01 quota year did not exceed quota for the first time since 1990.

50 European markets in 2001 were characterised by buoyant butter prices being carried forward from 2000 but then falling in the second half of the year to a 20-month low. Consequently, intervention was opened in eight countries, including the UK, by December with sizeable amounts being sold into store. EU intervention stocks of butter reached 53 thousand tonnes in December (about 11 thousand tonnes in the UK). The opening of intervention and an increase in November in the level of export refunds helped stabilise butter prices.

51 Skimmed milk powder (SMP) prices entered 2001 well above support levels and during the first half of the year export refunds for SMP and whole milk powder (WMP) were cut as EU prices came into line with world prices. However, in the second half of 2001, prices for milk powders on world markets dropped dramatically, making EU exports uncompetitive. This, along with poor demand for SMP for use in animal feed, resulted in EU prices for SMP falling below intervention levels. Due to intervention being closed until March 2002, no SMP could be entered. The Commission increased export refunds for SMP and WMP in November and again in December in response to poor export sales and falling world prices.

52 There were some signs towards the end of 2001 that falling commodity prices were feeding through to the UK farmgate price of milk, which had otherwise gradually risen during 2001 to over 20 pence per litre from the exceedingly low levels that occurred in 2000.

Hen Eggs
(Tables 5.19)

53 Overall value of production of eggs for human consumption increased by 9.5 per cent in 2001. The total volume of egg production for human consumption rose by 6.9 per cent in 2001. Within this rise, processed eggs fell by 0.2 per cent. Eggs sold in shell, which account for 82 per cent of the eggs sold for human consumption in 2001, rose by 8.4 per cent. The average egg price rose by 2.5 per cent in 2001.

UK egg production
million dozen

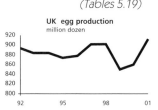

TABLE 5.17 Milk

Enquiries: Janine Horsfall on 01904 455092   email: janine.l.horsfall@defra.gsi.gov.uk

Million litres (unless otherwise specified)   *Calendar years*

	Average of 1990-92	1997	1998	1999	2000 (a)	2001 (provisional)
Population and Yield						
Dairy herd (annual average, '000 head) (b)	2 797	2 490	2 461	2 445	2 354	2 266
Average yield per dairy cow (litres per annum)	5 174	5 788	5 774	5 964	5 978	6 308
Production						
Production of milk from the dairy herd (c)	14 470	14 413	14 210	14 581	14 071	14 294
Production of milk from the beef herd (c)	8	7	7	7	7	7
less on farm waste and milk fed to stock	278	285	280	285	277	281
Volume for human consumption	14 200	14 135	13 937	14 303	13 801	14 020
Value of production (£ million)	2 836	3 154	2 709	2 653	2 393	2 818
of which:						
milk (d)	2 776	3 076	2 656	2 586	2 300	2 642
milk products (e)	97	92	84	76	85	96
agrimonetary compensation	..	..	..	..	22	79
less levies (f)	38	14	32	9	15	..
Prices (pence per litre) (g)						
Farmgate price of milk excluding bonus payments	..	21.95	19.26	18.30	16.91	19.15
Farmgate price of milk including bonus payments	..	22.12	19.37	18.35	16.93	19.16
Supply and Use (h)						
Production	14 478	14 420	14 217	14 588	14 078	14 301
Imports	..	128	129	111	105	61
Exports	71	290	373	465	445	352
Total domestic use	14 407	14 258	13 973	14 234	13 738	14 010
of which:						
for liquid consumption	6 737	6 748	6 739	6 853	6 768	6 726
for manufacture	7 196	7 059	6 821	6 988	6 550	6 820
of which:						
butter (i)	278	284	281	290	270	265
cheese	3 280	3 371	3 257	3 297	3 032	3 456
cream (i)	260	263	263	271	266	263
condensed milk (j)	725	692	643	603	522	533
milk powder - full cream	512	822	809	853	932	842
milk powder - skimmed	1 645	1 146	1 101	1 123	889	794
other	496	482	467	549	640	668
Dairy wastage and stock change	..	112	80	56	91	130
Other uses (k)	..	338	333	338	329	333

source: DEFRA Statistics website, www.defra.gov.uk/esg

(a) 366 days.

(b) Dairy herd is defined as cows and heifers in milk plus cows in calf but not in milk, kept mainly for producing milk or rearing calves for the dairy herd.

(c) Excludes suckled milk.

(d) Value of milk sold for processing off farm. Excludes milk processed on farm and sold direct to the consumer.

(e) Value of milk products manufactured on farm for sale direct to the consumer.

(f) Comprising milk co-responsibility levy from 1977 to 1993 and milk superlevy.

(g) The farmgate price is the average price received by milk producers, net of delivery charges. No deduction is made for superlevy. In the current year, estimated bonuses for April to December have been included.

(h) Aggregated data from surveys run by DEFRA, SEERAD and DARD, NI on the utilisation of milk by dairies.

(i) Includes the utilisation of the residual fat of low fat liquid milk production.

(j) Includes condensed milk used in the production of chocolate crumb and in the production of machine skimmed milk.

(k) Includes farmhouse consumption, milk fed to stock and on farm waste. Excludes suckled milk.

TABLE 5.18 Milk products

Enquiries: Janine Horsfall on 01904 455092   email: janine.l.horsfall@defra.gsi.gov.uk
This data shows UK production and supplies of milk products manufactured by both dairy companies and on farm. The data is
quoted in thousand tonnes and is not directly comparable with the data shown in table 5.17 which is quoted in million litres.

Thousand tonnes (unless otherwise specified)   *Calendar years*

		Average of 1990-92	1997	1998	1999	2000	2001 (provisional)
Butter (a) (b)							
Production (c)		137	139	137	141	132	129
Imports from:	the EU	57	66	57	67	80	75
	the rest of the world	58	45	48	47	38	40
Exports to:	the EU (d)	38	46	50	50	39	38
	the rest of the world	5	28	15	6	6	5
Total new supply (d)		209	175	176	199	204	202
Increase in stocks (e)		3	- 7	4	11	- 5	5
Total domestic uses (d) (e)		207	182	172	187	209	197
Production as % of total new supply for use in UK		65%	79%	78%	71%	64%	64%
Closing stocks (e)		67	7	11	22	17	22
Cheese							
Production (c)		320	377	366	368	340	385
Imports from:	the EU	191	210	225	236	225	241
	the rest of the world	18	30	32	41	30	32
Exports to:	the EU	27	43	45	49	48	55
	the rest of the world	20	10	10	13	10	11
Total new supply		483	563	567	584	536	593
Increase in stocks		1	2	- 10	1	-	14
Total domestic uses		481	561	577	583	536	579
Production as % of total new supply for use in UK		66%	67%	64%	63%	63%	65%
Closing stocks (f)		24	19	9	10	10	23
Cream - fresh, frozen, sterilized							
Production (b) (c)		241	268	266	275	270	267
Imports from:	the EU	3	11	11	8	10	16
	the rest of the world	-	-	-	-	-	-
Exports to:	the EU	27	91	100	95	86	89
	the rest of the world	4	1	1	1	1	1
Total new supply		213	187	176	188	193	193
Increase in stocks		..	..	..	..	..	..
Total domestic uses		213	187	176	188	193	193
Production as % of total new supply for use in UK		113%	144%	151%	146%	140%	138%
Closing stocks		..	..	..	..	..	..
Condensed milk (g)							
Production		203	214	192	177	162	166
Imports from:	the EU	12	13	13	14	14	14
	the rest of the world	-	-	-	-	-	-
Exports to:	the EU	10	33	43	38	29	29
	the rest of the world	42	30	21	13	3	3
Total new supply		163	164	141	139	144	148
Increase in stocks		- 2	- 1	- 1	1	- 1	7

TABLE 5.18 *cont.*

Thousand tonnes (unless otherwise specified)   *Calendar years*

	Average of 1990-92	1997	1998	1999	2000	2001 (provisional)
Total domestic uses	164	166	141	138	145	141
Production as % of total new supply for use in UK	124%	130%	136%	127%	112%	112%
Closing stocks	10	7	7	8	7	14
Milk powder - full cream						
Production	78	96	97	102	105	89
Imports from: the EU	3	10	10	10	11	11
the rest of the world	-	-	-	-	-	-
Exports to: the EU	22	18	26	28	27	27
the rest of the world	47	88	80	64	74	74
Total new supply	13	1	1	20	15	- 1
Increase in stocks	- 1	1	-	-	- 1	5
Total domestic uses	14	-	1	20	16	- 7
Closing stocks	3	3	3	3	2	7
Skimmed milk powder						
Production	138	109	107	102	83	74
Imports from: the EU	13	13	11	14	13	20
the rest of the world	-	-	-	-	-	-
Exports to: the EU (d)	56	12	21	30	77	28
the rest of the world	17	33	13	30	35	5
Total new supply (d)	79	77	85	57	- 16	62
Increase in stocks	- 3	18	27	- 11	- 66	8
Total domestic uses (d)	81	59	57	68	50	54
Production as % of total new supply for use in UK	181%	141%	127%	180%	- 527%	120%
Closing stocks	18	55	82	71	5	14

source: DEFRA Statistics website, www.defra.gov.uk/esg

(a) Includes butter other than natural (i.e. butterfat and oil, dehydrated butter and ghee).

(b) Includes production from the residual fat of low fat milk products.

(c) Includes farmhouse manufacture.

(d) These figures include the use of these products for animal feed.

(e) In addition to stocks in public cold stores surveyed by DEFRA, closing stocks include all intervention stocks in private cold stores. Total domestic uses does not equate exactly with consumption since changes in unrecorded stocks are not included in the calculation.

(f) Cheese stocks held in public cold stores. Public coldstores make their storage space available to the public or to the Rural Payments Agency, formerly the Intervention Board. The ownership of the store whether public or private is irrelevant.

(g) Includes condensed milk used in the production of chocolate crumb and in the production of sweetened and unsweetened machine skimmed milk.

TABLE 5.19 Hen Eggs

Enquiries: Adrian Roberts on 01904 455074   email: adrian.roberts@defra.gsi.gov.uk

Calendar years

	Average of 1990-92	1997	1998 (a)	1999	2000	2001 (provisional)
Production						
Volume of production of eggs (million dozen)	897	902	902	850	860	913
of which: eggs for human consumption	809	794	792	743	752	803
eggs for hatching (b)	76	95	94	93	94	95
hatching eggs for export (c)	2	4	7	5	5	6
waste	9	8	9	8	9	9
Production for Human Consumption:						
Number of Fowls laying eggs for eating (millions) (d)	36.4	33.3	33.1	30.9	31.2	33.5
Average yield per layer (number of eggs per bird per year)	267	286	287	288	289	287
Value of production of eggs for human consumption (£ million) (e)	405	415	381	344	371	406
Prices						
Average price (p per dozen)	50.0	52.2	48.1	46.3	49.4	50.6
UK graded egg price weighted average (f)	38.5	39.6	36.3	34.2	36.4	37.8
Supply and use (million dozen)						
UK production of eggs for human consumption	809	794	792	743	752	803
of which: eggs sold in shell	724	669	662	605	615	667
eggs processed	85	126	130	139	136	136
Imports from (g): the EU	54	69	63	68	91	110
the rest of the world	-	2	1	2	2	1
Exports to (g): the EU	14	20	30	15	15	10
the rest of the world	1	6	7	3	3	2
Total new supply	849	838	819	795	827	902
Production of eggs for human consumption as % of total new supply for use in UK	95%	95%	97%	93%	91%	89%

source: DEFRA Statistics website, www.defra.gov.uk/esg

(a) For comparability with other years, the figures for 1998 have been adjusted from a 53 week to a 52 week basis.

(b) Eggs for hatching are not valued as they are included in the final value of poultry.

(c) Hatching eggs for export are valued in the poultry table 5.16

(d) Population is implied from Gross production and Average yield and hence differs from the census figures in table 3.2

(e) Excludes value of eggs for hatching.

(f) Represents the UK Packer to Producer Price excluding bonus. Takes account of all egg systems - laying cages, free range, barn.

(g) Includes shell egg equivalent of whole (dried, frozen and liquid) egg, egg yolk and albumen.

Purchased feedingstuffs and seeds

Purchased feedingstuffs | **54**

(Table 5.20)

The value for compound usage rose by 9.3 per cent in 2001 to £1,404 million. The increase is as a result of a 3.4 per cent increase in usage and higher prices.

UK feed costs

£m

55 The increase in usage is mainly due to a 7.7 per cent increase in cattle compounds. As the largest sector it has the greatest effect on the total usage. Several factors have led to this increased usage including movement restrictions due to foot and mouth disease, shortages of quality silage and late housing of cattle in the spring. In addition, feeding of compounds did not fall in line with reduced dairy herd sizes due to the below quota position.

Purchased seeds | **56**

(Table 5.21)

The total cost of purchased seeds in 2001 increased by 7.9 per cent to £292 million, with an overall increase in price offsetting the slight fall in volume. The volume of seed for wheat returned to the higher levels of 1999 whilst the volume of seed potatoes fell.

TABLE 5.20 Feedingstuffs (including direct inter-farm and intra-farm transfer)

Enquiries: Tim Marsh on 01904 455061   email: tim.marsh@defra.gsi.gov.uk

Thousand tonnes (unless otherwise specified)   *Calendar years*

	Average of 1990-92	*1997*	*1998*	*1999*	*2000*	*2001 (provisional)*
Compounds:						
cattle	..	3 809	3 732	4 176	3 940	4 242
calves	..	227	202	187	190	187
pigs	..	2 673	2 751	2 469	2 113	1 980
poultry (a)	..	3 273	3 129	3 181	3 057	3 219
other	..	703	725	874	736	732
Total (b)	..	10 594	10 412	10 750	9 891	10 228
Straight concentrates (i.e. cereals, cereal offals, proteins and other high energy feeds)	..	5 649	5 815	6 019	6 562	6 301
Non-concentrates (low-energy bulk feeds expressed as concentrate equivalent) (c)	..	535	527	526	525	525
Inter/intra farm transfer	3 115	3 332	3 490	3 151	2 720	2 801
Total all purchased feedingstuffs	19 636	20 110	20 243	20 446	19 698	19 855
Value of purchased feedingstuffs (£ million) (d)	2 858	2 804	2 444	2 261	2 108	2 297

source: DEFRA Statistics website, www.defra.gov.uk/esg

(a) This item includes poultry feed produced by 'retail' compounders, but excludes production from integrated poultry units which are included within the straight data.

(b) Including imports, less exports

(c) Brewers and distillers grains, hay, milk by-products and other low-energy bulk feeds expressed in terms of equivalent tonnage of high energy feeds.

(d) See Table 6.1 for a breakdown of this total.

TABLE 5.21 Purchased seeds

Enquiries: Dave Fernall on 01904 455058   email: david.fernall@defra.gsi.gov.uk

Thousand tonnes (unless otherwise specified)   *Calendar years*

	Average of 1990-92	1997	1998	1999	2000	2001 (provisional)
Cereals (a)	483	443	387	433	391	437
Grass and clover	11	13	12	11	11	11
Root and fodder crops	44	42	44	44	46	60
Potatoes (b)	501	444	432	440	448	378
Vegetable and other horticultural seeds (c)	122	128	132	138	144	143
Total purchased seeds	1 162	1 070	1 007	1 066	1 041	1 030
Total value of all purchased seeds (£ million)	318	337	331	331	271	292

source: DEFRA Statistics website, www.defra.gov.uk/esg

(a) Restricted to the purchase of certified seed only.

(b) Includes farm-saved seed.

(c) Includes bulbs and seeds for hardy nursery stock, flowers, sugar beet and oilseed rape.

Chapter **6** Accounts

TIFF **1** Total Income From Farming (TIFF) in 2001 in the UK is estimated to have risen by 13 per cent (11 per cent in real terms) compared to its 2000 level. TIFF represents business profits plus income to farmers, partners and directors and those with an entrepreneurial interest in the business. In real terms TIFF is forecast to be 72 per cent below its peak in 1995 (after more than doubling between 1990 and 1995).

2 TIFF is sensitive to small percentage changes in the values of outputs and inputs. This sensitivity, the provisional nature of the figures for the latest year and revisions made to previously published figures for earlier years, as methodology or data sources improve, all need to be borne in mind when using the figures.

Treatment of foot **3** TIFF excludes compensation for livestock destroyed for foot and mouth disease
and mouth losses control and associated welfare purposes. This is a consequence of the decision taken by the Office for National Statistics.

4 The Office for National Statistics decided that destroyed livestock should be treated as "exceptional losses", as defined in the European System of Accounts 1995, and shown in the other changes in the volume of assets account. It follows from this decision that all the compensation should be treated as capital transfers and not part of income. It is therefore shown in the capital account, table 6.4. In addition it also follows that the part-production of livestock being reared for slaughter prior to the point of cull is included in the production account and contributes to output and income. Destroyed breeding livestock do not contribute to output or income (although their depreciation up until the point of culling is allowed for).

Aggregate **5** The Aggregate Agricultural Account provides details of the industry's outputs,
Agricultural Account inputs and generation of income. It conforms to internationally agreed accounting
(Tables 6.1 and 6.2, Charts principles required by both UK national accounts and by Eurostat.
6.1 and 6.2)

6 Table 6.1 shows the full account at current prices with Chart 6.1 showing how the main aggregates in the account are related. Table 6.2 shows the value, price and volume changes between 2000 and 2001. Changes in value are shown in Chart 6.2.

Chart 6.1 Main components of the aggregate account

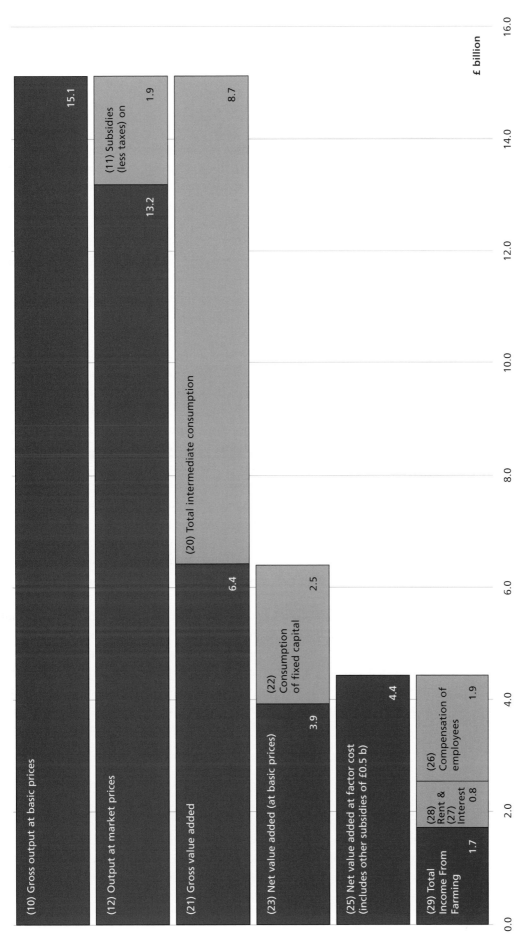

(10) Gross output at basic prices — 15.1

(12) Output at market prices — 13.2

(11) Subsidies (less taxes) on — 1.9

(21) Gross value added — 8.7

(20) Total intermediate consumption — 6.4

(22) Consumption of fixed capital — 2.5

(23) Net value added (at basic prices) — 3.9

(25) Net value added at factor cost (includes other subsidies of £0.5 b) — 4.4

(26) Compensation of employees — 1.9

(28) Rent & (27) Interest — 0.8

(29) Total Income From Farming — 1.7

£ billion

0.0   2.0   4.0   6.0   8.0   10.0   12.0   14.0   16.0

7 These tables show estimates of:

(a) Output at basic prices by product and the total at market prices after deducting subsidies;

(b) Transactions that take place wholly within the agricultural industry;

(c) Inputs – intermediate consumption, consumption of fixed capital (i.e. the reduction in value of capital assets due to depreciation), compensation of employees, rent and interest payments.

8 The value of output (including subsidies directly related to products) was slightly higher, up 0.7 per cent. The volume was 6.0 per cent lower with reduced production of cereals due to wet weather in the winter of 2000/2001 and of livestock due to foot and mouth disease. The prices received by farmers were 7.1 per cent higher due mainly to price rises for milk, potatoes, vegetables, sugar beet, oilseed rape and wheat.

9 A reduction in the output value of *livestock* of 11 per cent or £553 million in 2001 was mainly attributable to foot and mouth disease. The decrease was greatest in *sheep and lambs* where there was also a drop in direct subsidy payments resulting in an overall fall in output value of 35 per cent or £334 million. Floods and an exceptionally wet autumn in 2000 led to a significant reduction in the output value of *cereals* with *wheat* being most affected. Although *wheat* prices rose in 2001, falls in yield and area resulted in a decrease in output value of 23 per cent or £356 million. High prices for *potatoes* harvested in 2000 led to a rise in output value of 32 per cent or £146 million. The output value of *milk* rose by 18 per cent or £425 million due to a large increase in price.

10 Direct subsidies less levies to the agricultural industry in 2001 amounted to £2.5 billion, 1.9 per cent more than in 2000. Full details can be found in Chapter 8.

11 Intermediate consumption cost farmers 2.6 per cent, or £221 million, more. They used less fertiliser and pesticides but more seeds. They had to re-sow in spring due to weather conditions using 6.3 per cent more seeds. Although they used 5.7 per cent less fertiliser on a smaller planted area, the price rose by 10 per cent resulting in an increase in expenditure of 4.2 per cent. Pesticides consumption fell by 6.5 per cent. Livestock farmers also faced increased costs. The price of feedingstuffs was 8.0 per cent higher because of higher cereals prices. General costs also rose as they coped with movement restrictions due to foot and mouth disease.

12 Gross Value Added for the industry, which represents its contribution to national GDP, was down in volume by 13 per cent because of the drop in outputs without a corresponding drop in inputs. However, due to price rises for some outputs, its value was down by only 1.8 per cent. This drop is in part due to the decoupling of some subsidies from products which removes them from output (e.g. the Hill Livestock Compensatory Allowance paid per animal has been replaced by Less Favoured Area schemes paid per hectare).

13 Net Value Added at factor cost is the best measure of value added by the industry because it includes all subsidies (some are not included in output e.g. set-aside and agri-environment). It makes no allowance for interest, rent or labour costs. It increased by 3.7 per cent.

14 TIFF is derived by deducting interest, rent and paid labour costs from Net Value Added at factor cost. Interest payments were 8.5 per cent lower with rent and labour costs virtually unchanged. As a consequence TIFF showed a rise at current prices.

Balance sheet **15** The aggregate balance sheets for UK agriculture, Table 6.3, show the net worth of
(Table 6.3) the industry in terms of assets and liabilities at the end of each calendar year. Estimates for 2001, including the impact of foot and mouth disease, are not yet available.

Percentage changes

	Current prices		Real terms	
	1999/1998	2000/1999	1999/1998	2000/1999
Total assets	4.0	2.9	2.2	0.0
Total liabilities	3.0	-1.7	1.2	-4.5
Net worth	4.1	3.4	2.3	0.4

Current prices are net of depreciation but exclude the value of quotas.

Real terms at 1995 prices.

16 The rise in the total value of assets in 2000 was due to increases in the value of land and buildings (up 3.4 per cent), crops and stores (up 4.6 per cent) and breeding livestock (up 27 per cent, reversing the decline since 1996). These increases were partially offset by falls in the values of trading livestock (down 6.2 per cent), plant, machinery and vehicles (down 5.1 per cent) and debtors and cash deposits (down 3.9 per cent). The level of short term liabilities fell by 3.6 per cent while total long and medium term liabilities remained unchanged.

17 All indications suggest that there will be a substantial increase in net worth in 2001. Land and buildings is the most significant element in the valuation of assets. Despite foot and mouth disease land prices seem to have held up, although the level of sales has been depressed. Foot and mouth disease compensation amounting to £1.2 billion has been paid to farmers; this is expected either to increase the value of assets or reduce liabilities. Livestock valuations are expected to fall, with a greater decline in the value of trading livestock compared with breeding animals. Although livestock numbers have fallen prices for breeding livestock have increased, mitigating the decline in their value. Until the results of surveys which include information on liabilities become available, it is not possible to predict how these will change.

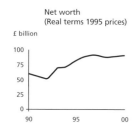

Net worth
(Real terms 1995 prices)

£ billion

18 Net worth increased appreciably in real terms between 1992 and 1996. Most of this can be explained by an increase in the value of the land and buildings component of assets, although some of the large rise in 1993 will have been due to the change to a new land price series (see below). Since 1996, when farm incomes plummeted, net worth has changed little. During the period 1970-1992, net worth fluctuated considerably, reaching its lowest value in 1992. The net worth of agriculture is now about 25 per cent lower compared with the highest level in 1973, when the UK joined the then European Community.

19 Values of land and buildings are not directly comparable with data prior to 1993. From 1993, for England and Wales, some transactions influenced by non-market considerations have been excluded. The new price series may not necessarily represent purely competitive conditions; however, in general it tends to be higher than the old series. In addition, land and buildings are now valued using the average price of land sold. As a result of both these changes, land and buildings (and consequently total assets) tend to have a higher valuation than previously. Due to the provisional nature of the published land price series, a weighted average of the land price in quarter 3 and quarter 4 of the balance sheet year is used to value land and buildings.

Accumulation accounts

20 Tables 6.4 and 6.5 form part of the accumulation accounts for the agriculture industry. The accumulation accounts include the capital account, the other changes in the volume of assets account, the revaluation account and the financial account. Table 6.4 contains elements of the capital account and the other changes in the volume of assets account. Table 6.5 shows elements of the revaluation account and changes in net worth due to changes in prices. The net worth shown in the balance sheets incorporates changes due to all of the accumulation accounts.

Capital account
(Table 6.4)

21 The capital account, table 6.4 shows estimates of changes in the assets held by the UK agricultural sector.

22 The provisional estimate of total gross fixed capital formation in buildings, works, plant, machinery and vehicles in 2001 is £1.2 billion. This is a small increase of £14 million or 1.2 per cent over 2000 due to an increase in plant and machinery investment. Gross fixed capital formation has fallen by around 30 per cent since 1997 due to the decline in incomes. Consumption of fixed non-livestock assets decreased by £10 million between 2000 and 2001.

23 Capital formation and capital consumption in livestock measure the output value due to the production of breeding animals and the depreciation of breeding animals (mainly dairy cows, beef cows, ewes, sows and egg laying poultry). In 2000 the production of breeding cattle was low as the breeding herd was in decline whereas in 2001 it was high due to restocking after foot and mouth disease. Therefore there was an increase in capital formation in livestock of £195 million. In contrast, consumption of fixed capital in livestock (approximated by assuming that all depreciation takes place at the times animals leave the breeding herds) increased by only £19 million.

24 Changes in inventories contribute to income. Stocks of crops were lower because of the reduction in production of cereals and other crops. Stocks of work-in-progress animals were higher because animals culled due to foot and mouth disease measures have not been removed from the inventories but have been shown as exceptional losses. Increases in breeding cattle, breeding sheep and slaughter pigs were only partly offset by reductions in slaughter cattle and slaughter sheep.

25 This table also brings together information on the balance sheet value of foot and mouth disease losses and the value of compensation and welfare disposal payments (see paragraph 4). Capital transfers to the UK agriculture industry amounted to £1.35 billion in 2001, of which foot and mouth disease payments accounted for £1.27 billion. Livestock destroyed due to foot and mouth disease measures are treated as exceptional losses and should be deducted from within the capital amount. Whilst these balance sheet losses have been valued at £0.46 billion this figure cannot be compared with the foot and mouth disease payments. The vast majority of the foot and mouth compensation was based on individual valuations whereas the balance sheet value of losses are based on average prices observed in livestock markets prior to the outbreak and do not relate specifically to the destroyed animals. Also the conventional approach to the balance sheet valuation is not designed to cope with the involuntary nature of these losses.

26 It is therefore not yet possible to show the impact of foot and mouth disease on the net worth of the industry. Further investigation of the balance sheet valuation will be undertaken as more statisical data becomes available. The EU auditors and NAO studies of foot and mouth disease payments, together with our own planned independent study, will provide information on the compensation process.

Valuation of exceptional losses
(Table 6.4)

27 The balance sheet valuations of the destroyed livestock have been prepared using the normal methods, largely based on market price information available prior to the outbreak and reflecting prices for "average" animals in the herds and flocks. The balance sheet valuation does not allow for any changes in price that may have been caused by the foot and mouth outbreak, nor for any specific characteristics associated with the culled livestock. The unusual conditions not allowed for in the balance sheet valuation include:

- livestock markets being closed and exports restricted;

- many destroyed livestock would not have been traded at that stage in their lile cycle;

- destroyed livestock may have included a disproportionate number of higher value pedigree or hefted livestock;

- many destroyed breeding livestock would never have been traded through regular markets.

28 Balance sheet prices for livestock being reared for meat but not yet ready for slaughter were estimated from the prices observed in the livestock markets before the outbreak with an adjustment then made based on the price of finished livestock (which did not increase significantly at the outset or during the outbreak). The exceptional losses of livestock being reared for meat were valued at these estimated balance sheet prices. However, many destroyed livestock were not being reared for meat as they formed part of the breeding herd.

29 Balance sheet prices for breeding animals of all ages were estimated from the herd entry prices and the normal cull prices observed in the livestock markets before the outbreak. The mid-point between these two prices was used, assuming that on average breeding animals were halfway through their productive life. The entry prices are usually based on prices for young, breeding livestock traded in markets. In 2001, these entry prices were estimated based on trends up to the outbreak and then, following the closure of markets, through consultation within the industry; entry prices were estimated to be higher in 2001 than in 2000.

30 The balance sheet prices for breeding animals makes the assumption that they depreciate linearly from their entry price to their normal cull price i.e. that on average they are at the mid-point of the entry and cull price. Such an assumption does not apply for individual animals for which the pattern of depreciation is highly uncertain. The amounts paid in compensation to farmers for livestock that were destroyed under the Animal Health Act 1981 (AHA) were largely based on individual valuations at the time of the culls. These valuations were made by a large number of independent professional valuers operating as MAFF/DEFRA's appointed experts working on site, with the animals in view and with knowledge of the herd history, recent herd transactions and historical knowledge of market price obtainable for the breed and category of the animal being valued in the relevant geographic area. In contrast the balance sheet valuation uses the balance sheet prices for "average" animals in the herds and flocks.

Compensation and Welfare Disposal Payments
(Table 6.4)

31 The rules which govern the payment of AHA compensation for animals slaughtered as a result of foot and mouth disease are set out in the Schedule 3, paragraph 3(2) of the Act. This provides that the Minister shall pay compensation for animals slaughtered under the Act as follows: (a) where the animal slaughtered was affected with foot and mouth disease the compensation shall be the value of the animal immediately before it became so affected; or (b) in every other case, the compensation shall be the value of the animal immediately before it was slaughtered. "Value" is not defined but is interpreted as meaning the market value of the animal: that is to say, the amount the animal would have fetched at market had it been sold at the time when it was slaughtered.

32 As described above the amounts paid in compensation to farmers for livestock that were destroyed under the AHA were largely based on individual valuations at the time of the culls.

33 The payments made in relation to livestock, which were entered voluntarily into the Livestock Welfare Disposal Schemes, were based on a pre-specified rate. These payment rates were specifically intended not to reflect the value of the livestock entered, but to address severe welfare problems arising directly from FMD controls and provide an outlet for animals which could not be disposed of elsewhere.

34 An upward trend in the average level of compensation under the AHA through the first four months of the outbreak was reflected in the average valuation for cattle and sheep doubling over this period. The reasons for this are not clear. The introduction of the standard valuations may have contributed to this trend as they were set above average values (with the intention of 70 per cent of culled livestock being valued in this way in order to speed up eradication) and farmers retained the option of individual valuations. In addition as the outbreak continued there may have been the expectation that demand for replacement stock was increasing, thus pushing up prices, and hence valuations.

Accumulation accounts: Stock appreciation
(Table 6.5)

35 Table 6.5 shows estimates of stock appreciation in the industry. Stock appreciation (holding gains) measures the change in value between the time of production and the end of the accounting period due to changes in price. It is not included in the Aggregate Agricultural Account and does not contribute to income.

36 Total stock appreciation in 2001 fell to £15 million. The value of livestock fell by £102 million due to changes in prices after production had taken place. A fall in the value of work-in-progress of non-breeding livestock (£230 million) was partly offset by an increase in the value of work-in-progress of replacement animals (£128 million). There were relatively small changes in the values of stocks of crops except for wheat which rose by £86 million. This increase was due to higher prices, as a result of low production levels and higher demand, because of livestock movement restrictions.

Interest
(Table 6.6)

37 Table 6.6 shows details of interest charges payable on farmers" borrowings for agricultural purposes (including land purchases). These payments, net of interest on short-term deposits, are estimated to have decreased between 2000 and 2001 by £54 million to £579 million due to the reduction in interest rates over the year.

Volume of capital assets
(Table 6.7)

38 Table 6.7 shows volume indices for the formation and consumption of fixed capital assets (see also table 6.4). The total volume of gross fixed capital formation rose by 4.7 per cent in 2001 compared with 2000 and there was a rise in value of 13 per cent. The total value of consumption of fixed capital was virtually unchanged but volume fell by 4.1 per cent. Both these trends can be explained by increased prices.

39 Within capital formation, buildings and works showed the greatest decrease in volume (down 8.1 per cent) and corresponded with a 6.0 per cent decrease in the value of capital formation in buildings and works (from £344 million to £323 million). The volume of capital formation in vehicles increased by 4.4 per cent. With the value largely unchanged, this reflects a decrease in prices.

40 The substantial rise in the value of capital formation in livestock (over 50 per cent) was combined with a large rise in volume of 24 per cent. This represents a price increase of 22 per cent.

41 Since the dramatic decline in TIFF began in 1996, the volume of capital formation in all non-livestock assets has fallen. Initially the decline in buildings and works was slower than for other assets, but there was a marked fall from 1998 to 1999. Since 1999 only the volume of vehicles has increased. During the same period the volume of livestock assets peaked in 1997, fell until 2000 and rose in 2001 due to restocking after foot and mouth disease.

42 For consumption of fixed capital the trend is also downwards, although this generally started later, between 1998 and 1999. The exception is livestock which is inherently more volatile. A precipitate fall from 1996 to 1997 due to BSE (coinciding with an increase in capital formation in the same years) was followed by stagnation, then a large rise in 2000 with a fall back to earlier levels in 2001 because of foot and mouth disease.

TABLE 6.1 Production and income account at current prices

Enquiries: Jim Holding on 01904 455080   email: jim.holding@defra.gsi.gov.uk

£ million   *Calendar years*

	Average of 1990-92	1997	1998	1999	2000	2001 (provisional)
Output (a)						
1. Total production of cereals	2 439	2 907	2 502	2 326	2 338	2 019
wheat	1 599	1 851	1 652	1 525	1 580	1 222
barley	782	977	781	735	685	726
oats	54	71	61	58	65	64
rye, mixed corn & triticale	4	9	8	8	8	6
2. Total production of other crops	1 042	1 207	1 188	1 194	958	1 017
oilseed rape	292	406	417	371	246	275
linseed	46	52	68	132	34	16
sugar beet	324	329	298	280	252	255
hops	18	20	14	13	11	10
peas and beans for stockfeed	116	129	112	115	113	141
hay and dried grass	27	28	23	23	22	23
grass and clover seed	16	23	20	19	11	9
straw	165	169	184	188	218	236
unspecified crops (b)	39	52	51	53	51	51
3. Total production of potatoes	545	390	630	750	454	600
4. Total production of horticulture	1 780	1 838	1 905	1 941	1 785	1 928
vegetables	979	962	989	962	877	970
fruit	275	199	259	257	228	243
ornamentals	519	671	650	715	672	708
horticultural seeds	7	7	7	7	7	7
5. Total production of livestock	5 399	6 316	5 513	5 279	5 206	4 654
finished cattle and calves	1 998	2 276	1 982	2 048	2 000	1 809
finished sheep and lambs	1 104	1 194	1 130	1 025	960	625
finished pigs	1 082	1 204	888	788	794	751
poultry	1 097	1 494	1 365	1 272	1 303	1 317
other livestock	119	148	147	147	150	152
6. Total production of livestock products	3 308	3 629	3 135	3 045	2 810	3 260
milk	2 836	3 154	2 709	2 653	2 393	2 818
eggs (c)	405	415	381	344	371	406
clip wool	44	35	24	21	23	16
unspecified livestock products	23	25	21	26	23	19
7. Total capital formation in livestock	607	735	588	391	374	569
cattle	335	391	295	203	191	359
sheep	145	198	154	56	48	75
pigs	17	15	5	7	5	6
poultry	110	130	135	125	131	129

Table 6.1 *cont.*

£ million

	Average of 1990-92	1997	1998	1999	2000	2001 (provisional)
8. Total other agricultural activities	453	699	680	720	657	622
Contract Work	414	575	571	614	608	612
Leasing out Milk Quota	39	120	99	99	42	4
Leasing out Ewe Premium	-	4	4	4	3	2
Leasing out Suckler Cow Premium	-	1	6	3	4	5
9. Total inseparable non-agricultural activities	246	369	418	426	439	457
10. Gross output at basic prices	15 819	18 090	16 560	16 071	15 022	15 126
11. Total subsidies (less taxes) on product	638	2 588	2 436	2 396	2 180	1 943
12. Output at market prices (10-11) (e)	15 182	15 502	14 123	13 675	12 842	13 183
of which						
transactions within the agricultural industry						
feed wheat	90	77	79	64	33	38
feed barley	249	193	164	148	136	144
feed oats	20	12	12	14	12	12
seed potatoes	21	9	12	30	9	12
straw	156	160	173	176	205	222
contract work	414	575	571	614	608	612
leasing of quota	39	124	109	106	49	11
total capital formation in livestock	607	735	588	391	374	569
Intermediate consumption (e)						
(Expenditure net of reclaimed VAT)						
13. Total feedingstuffs	2 858	2 804	2 444	2 261	2 108	2 297
compounds (d)	1 722	1 772	1 524	1 402	1 285	1 404
straights (d)	776	750	667	632	642	699
feed purchased from other farms	359	282	254	227	181	194
14. Total seeds	318	337	331	331	271	292
cereals	119	103	84	94	82	94
other	198	233	247	237	189	198
15. Total fertilisers and lime	892	983	827	752	753	785
16. Pesticides	531	675	655	620	611	555
17. Total farm maintenance (e)	273	370	328	320	298	309
occupier	210	298	257	251	231	242
landlord	64	72	71	69	68	67
18. Energy	565	630	599	624	730	717
machinery fuel and oil	329	397	368	402	488	492
power and fuel (mainly electricity)	236	233	231	222	242	224
19. Total miscellaneous expenses	2 861	3 896	3 800	3 847	3 716	3 751
machinery repairs	597	722	700	700	654	676
veterinary expenses and medicines	221	308	288	271	264	252
straw for bedding	156	160	173	176	205	222
contract work	414	575	571	614	608	612
leasing of quota	39	124	109	106	49	11
other farming costs (e) (f)	1 433	2 007	1 959	1 980	1 936	1 980
20. Total intermediate consumption	8 297	9 694	8 983	8 754	8 487	8 707
21. Gross value added (10-20)	7 522	8 395	7 576	7 317	6 535	6 418

continued

Table 6.1 *cont.*

£ million

Calendar years

	Average of 1990-92	1997	1998	1999	2000	2001 (provisional)
22. Total Consumption of Fixed Capital	2 297	2 685	2 594	2 441	2 492	2 499
buildings and works	632	671	683	700	690	679
landlord (e) (g)	114	85	83	78	77	76
other	517	586	600	622	612	603
plant, machinery and vehicles	1 090	1 327	1 333	1 320	1 285	1 285
cattle	310	393	316	207	288	320
sheep	139	155	106	68	93	83
pigs	16	15	9	8	7	6
poultry	110	123	147	137	129	127
23. Net value added (21-22)	5 225	5 710	4 983	4 877	4 043	3 919
24. Total other subsidies less taxes	- 31	113	138	238	232	514
animal disease compensation	6	15	24	28	41	29
set-aside	0	90	88	170	127	184
Agri-Environment schemes (h)	17	92	114	131	156	220
other including hill farm allowance (i)	-	-	-	..	..	164
taxes including vehicle licences	54	85	89	91	92	83
25. Net value added at factor cost (23+24)	5 195	5 823	5 120	5 114	4 275	4 433
26. Total compensation of employees (j)	1 759	1 930	1 977	2 028	1 897	1 914
27. Interest (k)	853	622	681	596	633	579
28. Net rent expenditure	162	256	250	238	232	230
rent paid (l)	162	336	331	321	310	302
rent received (m)	-	80	81	82	79	72
29. Total income from farming (25-26-27-28)	2 420	3 016	2 212	2 252	1 513	1 710

source: DEFRA Statistics website, www.defra.gov.uk/esg

(a) Output is net of VAT collected on the sale of non-edible products. Figures for total output include subsidies on products, but not other subsidies.

(b) Includes turf, other minor crops and arable area payments for fodder maize.

(c) Includes the value of duck eggs.

(d) For years prior to 1992 the split between compounds and straights has been estimated based on the split present in later years.

(e) Landlords' expenses are included within farm maintenance, miscellaneous expenditure and depreciation of buildings and works.

(f) Includes livestock and crop costs, water costs, insurance premiums, bank charges, professional fees, rates, and other farming costs.

(g) A more empirically based methodology for calculating landlords' depreciation was introduced in 2000. The new series has been linked with the old one using a smoothing procedure for the transition year of 1996.

(h) Includes Environmentally and Nitrate Sensitive Areas, Countryside Stewardship, Countryside Premium, Tir Cymen, Tir Gofal, Moorland, Habitat, Farm Woodland and Organic Farming Schemes.

(i) Includes guidance premium for beef and sheepmeat production, Pilot Beef and Sheep Extensification Scheme, and farm accounts grant as well as historic data for fertiliser and lime grant and payments to small scale cereal producers.

(j) Excludes the value of work done by farm labour on own account capital formation in buildings and works.

(k) Interest charges on loans for current farming purposes and buildings & works less interest on money held on short term deposit.

(l) Rent paid on all tenanted land (including 'conacre' land in Northern Ireland) less landlords' expenses, landlords' depreciation and the benefit value of dwellings on that land.

(m) Rent received by farming landowners from renting of land to other farmers less landlords' expenses. This series starts in 1996 following a revision to the methodology of calculating net rent.

Chart 6.2 Changes in output and inputs

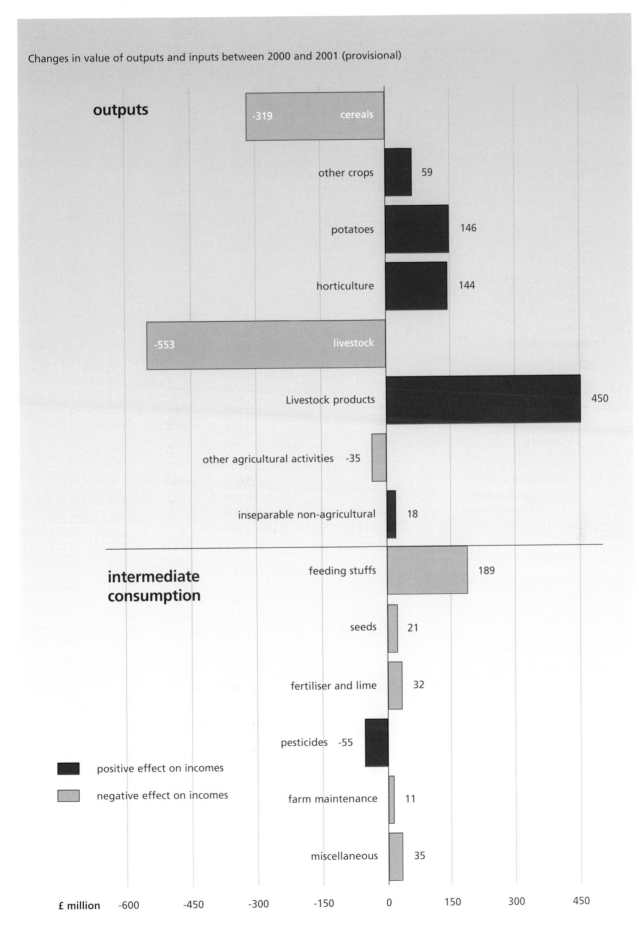

Changes in value of outputs and inputs between 2000 and 2001 (provisional)

outputs

cereals   -319

other crops   59

potatoes   146

horticulture   144

livestock   -553

Livestock products   450

other agricultural activities   -35

inseparable non-agricultural   18

intermediate consumption

feeding stuffs   189

seeds   21

fertiliser and lime   32

pesticides   -55

■ positive effect on incomes
▨ negative effect on incomes

farm maintenance   11

miscellaneous   35

£ million   -600   -450   -300   -150   0   150   300   450

2001

TABLE 6.2 Changes in outputs and inputs

Enquiries: Jim Holding on 01904 455080   email: jim.holding@defra.gsi.gov.uk

£ million

| | Current price value | | Changes % | | |
	2000	2001	value	volume	price
Outputs (a)					
1. Total production of cereals	2 338	2 019	- 14	- 20	8
wheat	1 580	1 222	- 23	- 30	11
barley	685	726	6	2	4
oats	65	64	- 1	- 4	3
rye, mixed corn & triticale	8	6	- 18	- 19	1
2. Total production of other crops	958	1 017	6	- 2	8
oilseed rape	246	275	12	5	6
linseed	34	16	- 53	- 10	- 48
sugar beet	252	255	1	- 10	12
hops	11	10	- 14	- 10	- 5
peas and beans for stockfeed	113	141	26	19	6
hay and dried grass	22	23	1	- 5	6
grass and clover seed	11	9	- 16	- 24	10
straw	218	236	9	- 5	14
unspecified crops (b)	51	51	1	- 12	15
3. Total production of potatoes	454	600	32	3	29
4. Total production of horticulture	1 785	1 928	8	- 1	9
vegetables	877	970	11	- 4	15
fruit	228	243	7	4	3
ornamentals	672	708	5	-	5
horticultural seeds	7	7	5	4	-
5. Total production of livestock	5 206	4 654	- 11	- 10	-
finished cattle and calves	2 000	1 809	- 10	- 11	2
finished sheep and lambs	960	625	- 35	- 30	- 6
finished pigs	794	751	- 5	- 8	3
poultry	1 303	1 317	1	3	- 2
other livestock	150	152	1	-	2
6. Total production of livestock products	2 810	3 260	16	2	13
milk	2 393	2 818	18	2	16
eggs (c)	371	406	10	9	-
clip wool	23	16	- 29	- 24	- 6
unspecified livestock products	23	19	- 17	- 17	- 1
7. Total capital formation in livestock	374	569	52	24	22
cattle	191	359	88	18	60
sheep	48	75	58	109	- 24
pigs	5	6	14	- 3	17
poultry	131	129	- 1	5	- 6
8. Total other agricultural activities	657	622	- 5	- 4	- 2
Contract Work	608	612	1	1	-
Leasing out Milk Quota	42	4	- 91	- 69	- 71
Leasing out Ewe Premium	3	2	- 29	- 6	- 25
Leasing out Suckler Cow Premium	4	5	13	3	10
9. Total inseparable non-agricultural activities	439	457	4	1	3
10. Gross output at basic prices	15 022	15 126	1	- 6	7
11. Total subsidies (less taxes) on product	2 180	1 943	- 11	- 15	5

continued

TABLE 6.2 *cont.*

£ million

	Current price value		Changes %		
	2000	2001	value	volume	price
12. Output at market prices (10-11) (e)	12 842	13 183	3	- 4	7
of which:					
transactions within the agricultural industry					
feed wheat	33	38	16	4	12
feed barley	136	144	6	3	3
feed oats	12	12	- 1	- 3	2
seed potatoes	9	12	33	- 27	81
straw	205	222	8	- 5	14
contract work	608	612	1	1	-
leasing of quota	49	11	- 78	- 59	- 47
total capital formation in livestock	374	569	52	24	22
Intermediate consumption (formerly known as Inputs) (e)					
(Expenditure net of reclaimed VAT)					
13. Total feedingstuffs	2 108	2 297	9	1	8
compounds (d)	1 285	1 404	9	3	6
straights (d)	642	699	9	- 4	14
feed purchased from other farms	181	194	7	3	4
14. Total seeds	271	292	8	6	1
cereals	82	94	15	12	2
other	189	198	5	4	1
15. Total fertilisers and lime	753	785	4	- 6	10
16. Pesticides	611	555	- 9	- 7	- 3
17. Total farm maintenance (e)	298	309	4	3	1
occupier	231	242	5	3	2
landlord	68	67	- 1	1	- 2
18. Energy	730	717	- 2	1	- 3
machinery fuel and oil	488	492	1	5	- 3
power and fuel (mainly electricity)	242	224	- 7	- 6	- 1
19. Total miscellaneous expenses	3 716	3 751	1	-	1
machinery repairs	654	676	3	-	3
veterinary expenses and medicines	264	252	- 5	- 3	- 2
straw for bedding	205	222	8	- 5	14
contract work	608	612	1	1	-
leasing of quota	49	11	- 78	- 59	- 47
other farming costs (e) (f)	1 936	1 980	2	2	-
20. Total intermediate consumption (e)	8 487	8 707	3	-	3
21. Gross value added (10-20)	6 535	6 418	- 2	- 13	13
22. Total Consumption of Fixed Capital	2 492	2 499	-	- 4	4
buildings and works	690	679	- 2	- 3	1
landlord (e) (g)	77	76	- 1	-	- 1
other	612	603	- 2	- 3	1
plant, machinery and vehicles	1 285	1 285	-	- 3	3
cattle	288	320	11	- 19	37
sheep	93	83	- 12	21	- 27
pigs	7	6	- 24	- 37	21
poultry	129	127	- 1	- 2	-
23. Net value added (21-22)	4 043	3 919	- 3	- 19	20

TABLE 6.2 *cont.*

£ million

	Current price value		Changes %		
	2000	2001	value	volume	price
24. Total other subsidies less taxes	232	514	122	..	..
animal disease compensation	41	29	- 29	..	..
set-aside	127	184	44	..	..
Agri-Environment schemes (h)	156	220	41	..	..
other including hill farm allowance (i)	..	164	..	..	..
taxes including vehicle licences	92	83	- 10	..	..
25. Net value added at factor cost (23+24)	4 275	4 433	4	..	..
26. Total compensation of employees (j)	1 897	1 914	1	- 2	3
27. Interest (k)	633	579	- 9	..	..
28. Net rent expenditure	232	230	- 1	..	..
rent paid (l)	310	302	- 3	..	..
rent received (m)	79	72	- 9	..	..
29. Total income from farming (25-26-27-28)	1 513	1 710	13	..	..

source: DEF.RA Statistics website, www.defra.gov.uk/esg

(a) Output is net of VAT collected on the sale of non-edible products. Figures for total output include subsidies on products, but not other subsidies.

(b) Includes turf, other minor crops and arable area payments for fodder maize.

(c) Includes the value of duck eggs.

(d) For years prior to 1992 the split between compounds and straights has been estimated based on the split present in later years.

(e) Landlords' expenses are included within farm maintenance, miscellaneous expenditure and depreciation of buildings and works.

(f) Includes livestock and crop costs, water costs, insurance premiums, bank charges, professional fees, rates, and other farming costs.

(g) A more empirically based methodology for calculating landlords' depreciation was introduced in 2000. The new series has been linked with the old one using a smoothing procedure for the transition year of 1996.

(h) Includes Environmentally and Nitrate Sensitive Areas, Countryside Stewardship, Countryside Premium, Tir Cymen, Tir Gofal, Moorland, Habitat, Farm Woodland and Organic Farming Schemes.

(i) Includes guidance premium for beef and sheepmeat production, Pilot Beef and Sheep Extensification Scheme, and farm accounts grant as well as historic data for fertiliser and lime grant and payments to small scale cereal producers.

(j) Excludes the value of work done by farm labour on own account capital formation in buildings and works.

(k) Interest charges on loans for current farming purposes and buildings & works less interest on money held on short term deposit.

(l) Rent paid on all tenanted land (including 'conacre' land in Northern Ireland) less landlords' expenses, landlords' depreciation and the benefit value of dwellings on that land.

(m) Rent received by farming landowners from renting of land to other farmers less landlords' expenses. This series starts in 1996 following a revision to the methodology of calculating net rent.

TABLE 6.3 Aggregate balance sheets for United Kingdom agriculture

Enquiries: Barbara Boize on 01904 455081   email: barbara.boize@defra.gsi.gov.uk

£ million   *As at December each year*

	Average of 1990-92	1997	1998	1999	2000	2001 (provisional)
At current prices						
Assets						
Fixed (a):						
Land and buildings (b)		38 419	84 038	84 643	90 605	93 665
Plant, machinery and vehicles		6 558	8 481	8 246	7 888	7 487
Breeding livestock		4 581	4 926	3 866	2 831	3 587
Total fixed		49 558	97 445	96 755	101 324	104 740
Current:						
Trading livestock		3 019	2 681	2 158	2 232	2 094
Crops and stores		2 428	2 668	2 593	2 139	2 238
Debtors, cash deposits		2 383	3 768	3 929	3 983	3 826
Total current		7 829	9 117	8 680	8 354	8 157
Total Assets		57 387	106 562	105 435	109 678	112 897
Liabilities (c) (d)						
Long and medium term:						
AMC and SASC (e)		756	1 288	1 321	1 381	1 406
Building Societies and Institutions		132	305	344	324	319
Bank loans		1 194	1 882	2 271	2 337	2 363
Family Loans		267	326	394	435	397
Other		195	185	206	174	183
Total long and medium term		2 546	3 986	4 536	4 651	4 667
Short term:						
Leasing		613	179	186	136	95
Hire purchase		143	662	549	467	434
Trade Credit		1 063	1 175	1 213	1 268	1 197
Bank overdrafts		3 481	2 598	2 775	3 061	3 035
Other		97	166	162	123	111
Total short term		5 398	4 780	4 884	5 055	4 872
Total Liabilities		7 944	8 767	9 421	9 706	9 540
Net worth		49 444	97 796	96 014	99 972	103 357
In real terms (as deflated by the RPI):						
indices, 1995 = 100						
Total assets		70	109	105	108	108
Total liabilities		105	98	102	104	99
Net worth		66	110	106	108	108

source: DEFRA Statistics website, www.defra.gov.uk/esg

(a) The valuations of land, buildings and breeding livestock are at average market prices; those of plant, machinery and vehicles are replacement cost, net of depreciation.

(b) Includes the value of owner-occupied and tenanted land and excludes dwelling houses apart from a proportion attributed to business use. See text for details of changes in valuation.

(c) Financial estimates are derived in part from a year-end analysis of farms in the Farm Business Survey. In practice, year-ends vary from December through to April, with concentrations of year-ends at end-December and end-March.

(d) Values for some liabilities are not strictly comparable with corresponding data prior to 1991. The revisions have resulted in an estimated increase of 8-9 per cent in net worth in 1991 and 1992.

(e) Agricultural Mortgage Company and Scottish Agricultural Securities Corporation.

2001

TABLE 6.4 Capital account

Enquiries: Stuart Platt on 01904 455054   email: stuart.platt@defra.gsi.gov.uk

£ million   *Calendar years*

	Average of 1990-92	1997	1998	1999	2000	2001 (provisional)
Gross fixed capital formation	1 972	2 523	2 032	1 639	1 562	1 771
Acquisitions less disposals of non-livestock assets:	1 365	1 788	1 444	1 248	1 188	1 202
buildings and works	492	551	505	365	344	323
plant and machinery	720	1 020	769	723	678	713
vehicles	153	217	170	161	166	165
Capital formation in livestock (a):	607	735	588	391	374	569
cattle	335	391	295	203	191	359
sheep	145	198	154	56	48	75
pigs	17	15	5	7	5	6
poultry	110	130	135	125	131	129
Consumption of fixed capital	2 297	2 685	2 594	2 441	2 492	2 499
Non-livestock assets:	1 721	1 998	2 016	2 020	1 974	1 964
buildings and works	632	671	683	700	690	679
plant and machinery	915	1 111	1 113	1 103	1 078	1 090
vehicles	175	216	220	218	207	194
Livestock (b):	575	687	578	420	517	536
cattle	310	393	316	207	288	320
sheep	139	155	106	68	93	83
pigs	16	15	9	8	7	6
poultry	110	123	147	137	129	127
Changes in inventories	- 33	37	- 97	25	- 80	- 118
stocks of crops	1	17	- 87	29	3	- 138
work-in-progress livestock	- 35	19	- 10	- 4	- 84	21
Total income from farming (1)	2 420	3 016	2 212	2 252	1 513	1 710
Capital Transfers (2)	150	112	3	25	19	1 346
Foot and mouth disease payments:	..	..	..	..	..	1 274
culled cattle	..	..	..	..	..	650
culled sheep	..	..	..	..	..	401
culled pigs	..	..	..	..	..	14
welfare disposals of cattle	..	..	..	..	..	125
welfare disposals of sheep	..	..	..	..	..	64
welfare disposals of pigs	..	..	..	..	..	15
other livestock (culled and welfare)	..	..	..	..	..	5
Other capital transfers	88	110	74	18	12	65
Capital grants	62	2	9	7	7	6
Exceptional Disposals (3) (due to foot and mouth) (c):	..	..	..	..	..	(d) 465
breeding cattle	..	..	..	..	..	177
slaughter cattle	..	..	..	..	..	121
breeding sheep	..	..	..	..	..	91
slaughter sheep	..	..	..	..	..	53
breeding pigs	..	..	..	..	..	4
slaughter pigs	..	..	..	..	..	14
other livestock	..	..	..	..	..	5

source: DEFRA Statistics website, www.defra.gov.uk/esg

(a) Capital formation in livestock is estimated by valuing the number of entries to the breeding herds at the entry price less the disposal price.

(b) Consumption of fixed capital in livestock is estimated by valuing the disposals from the breeding herds at the entry price less the disposal price.

(c) Livestock culled due to foot and mouth disease measures are treated as exceptional losses as defined in the European System

of Accounts 1995. For further information see text.

(d) This figure cannot be compared with the foot and mouth disease payments. The vast majority of the foot and mouth compensation was based on individual valuations whereas the balance sheet value of losses are based on average prices observed in livestock markets prior to the outbreak and do not relate specifically to the destroyed animals. For further information see text.

TABLE 6.5 Stock appreciation

Enquiries: Jim Holding on 01904 455080   email: jim.holding@defra.gsi.gov.uk

£ million   *Calendar years*

	Average of 1990-92	1997	1998	1999	2000	2001 (provisional)
Livestock Production work-in-progress (non-breeders)						
cattle		- 279	- 158	89	- 78	- 107
sheep		- 89	- 84	35	12	- 50
pigs		- 77	- 58	40	98	- 74
poultry (a)		- 35	- 5	- 8	6	1
total		- 480	- 305	156	37	- 230
Replacement animals for breeding herds						
cattle		- 266	- 120	- 23	24	141
sheep		- 40	- 35	15	5	- 12
pigs		- 1	- 1	1	1	- 1
total		- 308	- 156	- 8	30	128
Crop production work-in-progress						
wheat		- 135	- 36	- 63	- 41	86
barley		- 66	4	- 21	- 8	- 9
potatoes		- 1	-	-	- 1	2
other crops (b)		-	- 15	- 41	16	7
total		- 202	- 47	- 125	- 35	87
Total stock appreciation		- 990	- 508	23	33	- 15

source: DEFRA Statistics website, www.defra.gov.uk/esg

(a) Broilers, ducks, geese and turkeys.

(b) Oats, oilseeds, apples and pears.

TABLE 6.6 Interest

Enquiries: Jane Hinton on 020 7270 8612   email: jane.hinton@defra.gsi.gov.uk

£ million (unless otherwise specified)   *Calendar years*

	Average of 1990-92	1997	1998	1999	2000	2001 (provisional)
Interest rates (percentage)						
average bank base lending rate in the UK (percentage)	12.0	6.6	7.2	5.3	6.0	5.1
average rate of interest on bank advances to agriculture (percentage)	14.6	9.1	9.7	7.7	8.3	7.4
Interest charges (all lending to the farm business) on:						
bank advances	668	412	483	409	447	..
AMC loans	114	112	113	109	119	..
instalment credit	23	74	69	53	49	..
leased assets	39	18	15	10	7	..
other credit (a)	54	50	49	50	49	..
less interest on deposits (b)	44	44	47	37	38	..
Total	853	622	681	596	633	579

source: DEFRA Statistics website, www.defra.gov.uk/esg

(a) Interest paid on other institutional credit and that from private sources.

(b) Interest earned on money held on short-term deposit.

TABLE 6.7 Changes in Volume of Capital Assets

Enquiries: Jane Hinton on 020 7270 8612   email: jane.hinton@defra.gsi.gov.uk

Calendar years

	Average of 1990-92	1997	1998	1999	2000	2001 (provisional)
Total volume of gross fixed capital formation						
1995=100						
Gross fixed capital formation:	80.8	89.4	75.7	66.1	61.0	63.8
non livestock:	75.1	84.9	67.0	56.9	53.2	52.4
buildings and works	95.8	100.4	89.6	62.1	54.6	50.2
plant and machinery	69.6	80.0	59.0	54.9	51.2	51.3
vehicles	61.3	76.3	58.7	55.6	60.1	62.7
livestock	93.9	104.6	103.2	96.3	84.8	105.5
Total volume of capital consumption						
1995=100						
Consumption of fixed capital	95.6	99.3	98.1	97.2	96.7	92.8
non livestock:	100.5	101.6	100.3	98.5	96.2	93.1
buildings and works	98.7	101.6	100.6	99.0	96.9	94.4
plant and machinery	102.4	101.0	99.1	97.0	94.3	90.7
vehicles	97.6	105.2	105.5	104.6	103.7	102.2
livestock	85.4	92.0	91.2	93.3	101.0	93.4

source: DEFRA Statistics website, www.defra.gov.uk/esg

Chapter 7 Productivity

Volume Indices
(Table 7.1)

1 The volume of production has increased by 22 per cent over the last 25 years. Production of wheat and poultry more than doubled in the same period. The volume of output in 2001 was 6.0 per cent lower than 2000, due mainly to reduced production of wheat and livestock.

2 In 2001, production of cereals was 20 per cent down compared to 2000. This was mainly due to poor weather conditions at the beginning of 2001 which resulted in a drop in both yield and area. The volume of production of wheat fell by 30 per cent. Production of barley was slightly higher in 2001 due to more spring barley plantings. The volume of production of other crops declined by 1.6 per cent in 2001.

3 The volume of output of potatoes increased by 2.8 per cent in 2001 compared to 2000 and is roughly at the same level as it was in 1990. Horticulture production has declined over the last 25 years mainly due to a long-term decline in fruit production. However, in 2001 production of fruit increased by 3.8 per cent whilst vegetable production fell by 3.6 per cent.

4 Production of livestock fell by 10 per cent in 2001. Whilst production of cattle, sheep and pigs decreased substantially, the volume of production of poultry increased. Sheep production fell by 30 per cent. The fall in cattle, sheep and pig production was mainly due to foot and mouth disease. Cattle and calves which were disposed of in the Over Thirty Month Scheme and the Calf Processing Aid Scheme (which ran from 22 April 1996 until 31 July 1999) have not been counted towards the volume of output. Foot and mouth losses were treated as exceptional. This means that the volume of part produced animals – for slaughter or the breeding herd – that were culled were included in output.

5 Milk production has been fairly steady since 1984 due to the quota system. Production of eggs has increased since 1999 with the largest increase in 2001 (9.2 per cent on 2000).

6 Overall the volume of inputs has increased by 13 per cent over the last 25 years. In 2001, inputs stayed at roughly the same level as 2000. There were reductions in consumption of both pesticides and fertilisers. Consumption of seeds was 6.3 per cent higher due to the high level of re-sowing in spring. Livestock farmers had higher inputs as they coped with movement restrictions due to foot and mouth disease.

7 As a result of the fall in outputs in 2001, and with little change in the volume of inputs, gross value added fell by 13 per cent.

Productivity

(Table 7.2 and Chart 7.1)

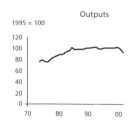

8 Productivity shows how efficiently inputs are converted into outputs. Since 1973 the productivity of the agricultural industry in the UK has increased by 36 per cent - see Chart 7.1 and Table 7.2. The measure used – total factor productivity – shows the volume of output leaving the industry per unit of all inputs, including fixed capital and paid labour; it encompasses all businesses engaged in farming activities, including specialist contractors. Increases in labour productivity have been the key factor driving this growth; since 1973 labour productivity has more than doubled. Labour productivity measures the volume of net value added per unit of all labour (paid and entrepreneurial).

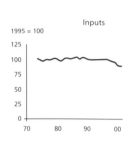

9 The increase in productivity since 1973 is explained by an increase in output without corresponding increases in inputs (including capital and labour). Throughout the nineties, output remained static but inputs decreased slightly.

10 However, in 2001 output decreased and inputs hardly changed compared to the previous year. Thus, labour productivity decreased by 17 per cent, whilst total factor productivity decreased by 6.1 per cent. The impact of foot and mouth disease and the measures taken to eradicate the disease reduced productivity in cattle and sheep production. Productivity in the arable sector was also reduced due to poor yields and re-sowing.

Paid labour

(Table 7.3)

11 Table 7.3 shows the cost and volume of paid labour relating to agricultural work only, excluding time spent on the construction of farm buildings. The total cost of paid labour increased by 0.9 per cent in 2001, arising from a decrease in the volume of paid labour input of 2.2 per cent and an average salary increase of 3.1 per cent. The volume of total labour decreased by 1.9 per cent during 2001. The increase in the statutory minimum wage agreed by the Agricultural Wages Board (AWB) was approximately 4.8 per cent in June 2000 and 4.4 per cent in October 2001. The annual negotiations of the AWB were postponed due to the foot and mouth disease outbreak and the new order in October 2001 represented an annualised increase of around 3.3%. The rate for adult casual workers was increased by just under 10 per cent in line with the National Minimum Wage.

12 The most significant fall in inputs is in compensation of employees (or paid labour) which has been reduced by 42 per cent since 1973, reflecting the outflow of labour from the industry.

13 Since the early 1980s there has been a shift in the composition of the labour force with an increase in part-time workers – rising from 25 per cent to nearly 40 per cent of the total.

Chart 7.1 Total factor productivity

(final output per unit of all inputs)

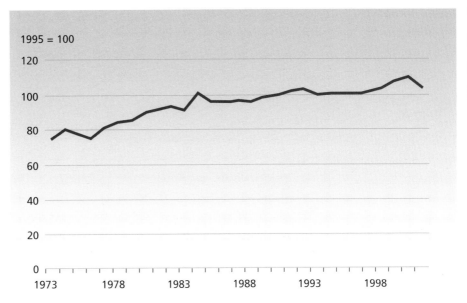

1995 = 100

TABLE 7.1 Output and input volume indices

Enquiries: Simone Pfuderer on 01904 455079   email: simone.pfuderer@defra.gsi.gov.uk

1995=100   *Calendar years*

	Average of 1990-92	1997	1998	1999	2000	2001 (provisional)
Outputs (a)						
1. Total production of cereals	99.7	106.7	103.5	100.4	108.8	87.0
wheat	99.3	104.2	107.6	103.5	116.3	81.1
barley	102.3	112.6	95.7	94.6	93.8	95.9
oats	80.7	93.6	95.2	87.0	103.5	99.4
rye, mixed corn & triticale	88.5	95.8	89.6	106.4	118.4	96.5
2. Total production of other crops	104.4	113.7	110.4	118.1	91.9	90.5
oilseed rape	100.3	131.1	135.0	136.8	93.7	98.5
linseed	183.5	131.7	177.6	374.9	52.9	47.7
sugar beet	105.8	131.5	118.6	125.5	107.7	97.0
hops	124.6	119.6	81.9	69.8	62.8	56.8
peas and beans for stockfeed	123.9	122.7	116.0	123.8	134.0	159.4
hay and dried grass	114.6	98.3	87.9	90.4	86.8	82.9
grass and clover seed	146.0	107.1	96.7	105.4	80.4	61.1
straw	75.8	74.4	70.8	62.6	65.9	62.7
unspecified crops (b)	106.9	74.0	64.4	61.9	53.9	47.5
3. Total production of potatoes	106.0	102.0	90.1	106.6	94.1	96.7
4. Total production of horticulture	111.9	96.0	96.8	99.1	93.4	92.4
vegetables	111.3	101.1	99.1	100.3	93.2	89.9
fruit	129.1	70.2	89.4	92.8	72.0	74.7
ornamentals	105.4	97.7	94.8	98.4	100.6	100.9
horticultural seeds	113.2	96.2	96.8	92.5	93.8	98.0
5. Total production of livestock	97.0	93.8	97.0	95.3	91.3	81.8
finished cattle and calves	101.8	78.9	81.4	82.4	80.4	71.2
finished sheep and lambs	105.2	93.5	100.0	99.3	94.3	65.6
finished pigs	99.3	110.2	112.2	102.4	86.4	79.2
poultry	82.5	106.0	108.4	105.8	106.2	109.8
other livestock	97.7	102.2	102.3	101.6	101.6	101.3

continued

Table 7.1 *cont.*

1995=100   *Calendar years*

	Average of 1990-92	*1997*	*1998*	*1999*	*2000*	*2001 (provisional)*
6. Total production of livestock products	103.1	100.8	99.6	101.3	99.5	101.8
milk	102.9	100.6	99.0	101.4	98.9	100.6
eggs (c)	104.5	103.7	105.1	101.3	105.7	115.4
clip wool	107.1	97.0	103.3	95.3	91.7	69.6
unspecified livestock products	114.2	89.8	79.4	94.5	82.6	68.8
7. Total capital formation in livestock	93.9	104.6	103.2	96.3	84.8	105.5
cattle	93.5	95.5	92.3	94.1	80.6	94.9
sheep	96.8	115.3	123.8	93.1	58.3	121.5
pigs	114.1	119.0	94.8	100.0	66.0	63.8
poultry	93.7	107.5	101.0	95.4	99.7	104.3
8. Total other agricultural activities	87.8	107.7	114.7	122.9	119.2	114.6
Contract Work	92.7	107.2	113.1	121.6	118.1	118.8
Leasing out Milk Quota	63.5	111.7	119.8	129.8	124.7	38.9
Leasing out Ewe Premium	83.3	52.6	62.3	61.4	57.2	53.9
Leasing out Suckler Cow Premium	50.1	66.0	452.6	241.9	236.8	244.2
9. Total inseparable non-agricultural activities	86.5	107.1	117.4	117.7	117.0	118.0
10. Gross output at basic prices	100.1	100.7	101.2	102.1	98.2	92.3
11. Total subsidies (less taxes) on product	110.7	107.1	108.6	109.6	103.4	87.7
12. Output at market prices (10-11) (e)	99.2	99.8	100.1	101.0	97.4	93.2
of which:						
transactions within the agricultural industry						
feed wheat	154.5	176.0	209.9	175.0	98.1	101.6
feed barley	118.0	125.8	123.5	113.6	111.3	115.1
feed oats	101.2	81.6	100.1	118.2	106.8	103.3
seed potatoes	117.8	86.4	79.3	84.4	76.2	55.9
straw	74.7	73.3	69.5	61.0	64.4	61.2
contract work	92.7	107.2	113.1	121.6	118.1	118.8
leasing of quota	63.4	109.0	121.3	127.5	122.4	50.2
total capital formation in livestock	93.9	104.6	103.2	96.3	84.8	105.5
Intermediate consumption (e) (Expenditure net of reclaimed VAT)						
13. Total feedingstuffs	94.3	94.9	95.5	96.2	91.6	92.5
compounds (d)	95.6	97.4	95.0	97.5	89.8	92.7
straights (d)	83.0	80.3	85.1	85.5	90.4	86.5
feed purchased from other farms	124.0	133.3	139.9	126.6	108.4	111.6
14. Total seeds	100.8	98.6	94.2	94.9	91.9	97.8
cereals	103.6	95.1	83.0	92.9	84.1	94.1
other	99.3	100.3	99.5	96.4	95.8	99.6
15. Total fertilisers and lime	104.0	108.4	103.1	96.7	86.9	82.0
16. Pesticides	97.9	107.9	111.8	107.6	113.0	105.6
17. Total farm maintenance (e)	83.3	96.2	84.6	83.7	76.8	78.8
occupier	78.5	96.1	82.1	81.4	73.1	75.5
landlord	105.1	96.7	95.0	93.3	92.1	92.7
18. Energy	96.9	99.8	108.2	103.7	94.3	95.2
machinery fuel and oil	94.6	99.6	107.4	104.1	91.0	95.1
power and fuel (mainly electricity)	100.6	99.8	109.2	102.6	99.8	93.6

Table 7.1 *cont.*

1995=100   *Calendar years*

	Average of 1990-92	1997	1998	1999	2000	2001 (provisional)
19. Total miscellaneous expenses	92.2	102.9	100.1	99.2	95.0	95.0
machinery repairs	99.2	93.8	91.2	89.2	81.5	81.8
veterinary expenses and medicines	78.6	104.1	96.5	90.6	89.2	87.0
straw for bedding	74.7	73.3	69.5	61.0	64.4	61.2
contract work	92.7	107.2	113.1	121.6	118.1	118.8
leasing of quota	63.4	109.0	121.3	127.5	122.4	50.2
other farming costs (e) (f)	96.4	109.4	103.8	102.3	98.0	99.9
20. Total intermediate consumption	94.4	100.6	99.4	98.1	93.5	93.2
21. Gross value added (10-20)	106.2	100.9	103.4	106.9	103.9	90.2
22. Total Consumption of Fixed Capital	95.6	99.2	98.0	97.1	96.6	93.0
buildings and works	98.7	101.6	100.6	99.0	96.9	94.4
landlord (e) (g)	105.1	60.0	57.0	55.8	55.2	55.2
other	97.7	111.3	111.0	109.2	106.8	103.7
plant, machinery and vehicles	101.7	101.5	99.9	98.1	95.6	92.9
cattle	85.8	93.7	89.3	91.2	108.6	88.5
sheep	80.5	79.3	81.1	92.1	96.1	116.6
pigs	99.6	101.1	111.1	97.8	83.4	52.5
poultry	94.7	102.9	109.8	104.4	99.2	97.4
23. Net value added (21-22)	110.7	101.5	105.8	111.7	107.4	86.9

source: DEFRA Statistics website, www.defra.gov.uk/esg

(a) Output is net of VAT collected on the sale of non-edible products. Figures for total output include subsidies on products, but not other subsidies.

(b) Includes turf, other minor crops and arable area payments for fodder maize.

(c) Includes the value of duck eggs.

(d) For years prior to 1992 the split between compounds and straights has been estimated based on the split present in later years.

(e) Landlords' expenses are included within farm maintenance, miscellaneous expenditure and depreciation of buildings and works.

(f) Includes livestock and crop costs, water costs, insurance premiums, bank charges, professional fees, rates, and other farming costs.

(g) A more empirically based methodology for calculating landlords' depreciation was introduced in 2000. The new series has been linked with the old one using a smoothing procedure for the transition year of 1996.

TABLE 7.2 Productivity

Enquiries: Simone Pfuderer on 01904 455079   email: simone.pfuderer@defra.gsi.gov.uk

volume indices 1995=100   *Calendar years*

Year	Final output (gross output less transactions within the agricultural industry)	Net value added per AWU of all labour (a)	Final output per unit of all inputs (including fixed capital and labour)
1990	99.3	97.8	99.2
1991	101.6	102.7	101.6
1992	101.6	107.5	102.2
1993	99.1	99.6	99.5
1994	99.9	101.9	100.2
1995	100.0	100.0	100.0
1996	99.6	99.5	99.9
1997	100.3	104.5	101.3
1998	100.6	110.8	103.5
1999	101.8	121.1	107.1
2000	98.4	124.2	109.2
2001 (provisional)	91.5	102.5	102.6

source: DEFRA Statistics website, www.defra.gov.uk/esg

(a) An annual work unit (AWU) represents the equivalent of an average full
time person engaged in agriculture.

TABLE 7.3 Costs and volumes of paid labour engaged in agricultural work

Enquiries: Jane Hinton on 020 7270 8612   email: jane.hinton@defra.gsi.gov.uk

Calendar years

	Average of 1990-92	1997	1998	1999	2000	2001 (provisional)
Paid labour costs (£ million) (a)	1 759	1 930	1 977	2 028	1 897	1 914
Annual Work Unit ('000) (b)						
Entrepreneurial Labour	254	239	236	229	222	218
Paid Labour	168	141	137	132	117	114
Total Labour Force	422	380	374	361	338	332

source: DEFRA Statistics website, www.defra.gov.uk/esg

(a) Includes payments in kind to workers and employer and
employee National Insurance contributions, redundancy
payments, Workers Pension Scheme (up to 1990) and the cost of
trainees.

(b) An annual work unit (AWU) represents the equivalent of an
average full time person engaged in agriculture.

Chapter **8** Subsidies

Introduction **1** In 1957, when the Treaty of Rome created the European Economic Community (EEC), provisions were included for a common agricultural policy (CAP). CAP's aims were to increase agricultural productivity, safeguard farmers' livelihoods, stabilise markets and guarantee the community's food supply. The mechanism adopted to achieve these aims was market regulation. World market prices dominated agricultural market prices so that when guaranteed prices were above world prices costs were met by the taxpayer.

2 This was the situation at the time the UK joined the EEC on 1 January 1973. Then, market support consisted of refunds for intra-Community and third country trade, costs of purchasing and storing intervention stocks, beef and sheep schemes and other marketing and production schemes. Market support was very successful in achieving the policy's aims, but it also created problems of commodity surpluses and rapidly increasing, even excessive, costs.

3 During the 1970s and 1980s reforms were introduced to curb spending and control over-production by modifying market support measures. In 1988 the UK introduced agri-environment schemes such as set-aside, the Farm Woodland Scheme and, to assist diversification, the Farm Diversification Grant Scheme.

4 In 1993 a major reform of the CAP was introduced. This radical reform represented a change in emphasis from supporting prices to direct aid payments to farmers, with consequent savings to consumers from price reductions. Rules for a new agrimonetary system and the Integrated Administration and Control System (IACS) for farmers claiming certain subsidies were introduced. And there was more help for social and environmental measures. In the UK schemes to protect heather moorland, encourage conversion to organic farming and create or improve wildlife habitats were introduced.

5 In 2000 the Agenda 2000 reform of the CAP, agreed in March 1999, was introduced. The aims were to cut prices and increase direct aid payments to safeguard agricultural incomes, lay the foundations for a comprehensive rural development policy and provide money for agri-environmental schemes.

6 In summary, there are three types of support. Firstly, there is market support in the form of intervention purchases and import tariffs. Market support measures affect the accounts for the agriculture industry through their impact on market prices. Details of the costs to the exchequer can be found in chapter 9. Secondly, there are direct payments linked to production which form the majority of the present subsidies. Thirdly, there are direct payments linked to rural development. Details of the direct payments are shown here.

Direct Subsidies and levies

(Table 8.1& 8.2)

7 Table 8.1 gives details of the values of the subsidies less levies paid directly to farmers that are included in the income account. The 2001 figures in all tables in this chapter are shown after modulation where appropriate. The provisional figures show that in 2001 the agricultural industry as a whole received nearly £2.5 billion in direct subsidies less levies, 1.9 per cent more than in 2000. There was a shift away from subsidies closely related to arable and livestock production to subsidies less related to the amount produced. In particular, there were increased payments under agri-environment schemes, set-aside and less favoured area support.

- Wheat payments were £109 million lower as less land was cultivated;

- The Over Thirty Month Scheme was £103 million lower as fewer animals were entered;

- Agrimonetary compensation paid to milk producers was £57 million higher;

- Set-aside payments were £57 million higher;

- Less favoured area support was over £50 million higher than payments under the previous scheme, the Hill Livestock Compensatory Allowance;

- Payments under agri-environment schemes were £64 million higher than last year.

Arable Area Payments

(Table 8.3)

8 The Arable Area Payments Scheme (AAPS) is a direct subsidy payable to arable producers. It was introduced in 1993, following the 1992 reform of the CAP, as compensation for reductions in market support. It has developed over the years and is being further modified as part of the Agenda 2000 reform of the CAP.

9 Table 8.3 shows direct subsidies and agrimonetary compensation made to the arable sector under the AAPS since 1999. The 2001 figures shown are after modulation has been applied.

10 In 2001 total payments made to farmers under AAPS fell by £50 million, or 4.7 per cent, to £1.0 billion compared to 2000. Payments for cereals fell, largely due to a 21 per cent reduction in the area claimed for wheat. The area claimed to set-aside increased by 53 per cent, with payments increasing by 44 per cent to £184 million. Agrimonetary compensation for 2001 totalled £29 million, down from £90 million in 2000. Modulation is estimated to reduce AAPS by £25 million in 2001.

Direct Support to Livestock Producers

(Table 8.4)

11 Five direct subsidies are currently available to livestock producers. These are:

- Beef Special Premium Scheme – a subsidy for male cattle;

- Suckler Cow Premium Scheme – a subsidy on female cattle forming part of a suckler breeding herd used for rearing calves for meat production;

- Extensification Payments Scheme – payments made to farmers who receive Beef Special Premium or the Suckler Cow Premium and meet specific stocking density levels;

- Slaughter Premium Scheme – a subsidy that provides direct support to all producers of domestic cattle;

- Sheep Annual Premium Scheme – a subsidy for breeding ewes.

12 In addition, Member States have additional funds, generally known as the Beef National Envelope, which can be used to assist beef producers in ways deemed most appropriate to the structure of the industry. The use made of the Beef National Envelope can be varied between constituent parts of the UK and from year to year.

13 Table 8.4 shows direct subsidies to the livestock sector with which agrimonetary compensation has been paid. The 2001 figures shown are after modulation has been applied. Tables 8.1 and 8.2 also show direct subsidies with which no agrimonetary compensation has been paid (for example, Slaughter Premium) and other payments that have been treated as income (for example, payments made under the Over Thirty Month Scheme).

14 Overall, provisional figures show that subsidies and other income payments to the livestock sector fell by 16 per cent in 2001 to £1.0 billion, due mainly to the ending of the Hill Livestock Compensatory Allowances in 2000 (replaced by land area based schemes), the closure of the Over Thirty Month Scheme for five months in 2001 and a fall in Sheep Annual Premium.

15 Subsidies to beef producers – Beef Special Premium, Suckler Cow Premium, Extensification Payments, Slaughter Premium and Beef National Envelope – rose by 18 per cent, but payments under the Sheep Annual Premium Scheme fell by 34 per cent owing to an increase in the EU average market price.

Modulation

16 EU legislation permits Member States to recycle, or modulate, a proportion of payments made direct to farmers under CAP commodity regimes. In order to secure a significant increase in funds for rural development measures, all direct payments made under CAP commodity regimes between 2001 and 2006 will be modulated.

17 Modulation was introduced at a flat rate of 2.5 per cent in the 2001 scheme year to help fund the Rural Development Programme (RDP). In other words, 2.5 per cent of subsidy payments (calculated after taking into account claims, any base reduction and any penalties) will be recycled to help fund the RDP. Every pound recycled in this way will be matched by a further pound from the government and the total returned through the RDP to the rural economy. On an accruals basis modulation is estimated to reduce arable and livestock subsidies by £44 million in 2001.

18 Modulation money that is being returned to farmers is included in schemes under the RDP. These include Countryside Stewardship, Tir Gofal, Countryside Premium, Environmentally Sensitive Areas and less favoured area schemes.

Agrimonetary compensation

19 Until 31 December 1998 most CAP support prices and amounts set in ecus were converted into national currency terms using special exchange rates known as green rates. Green rates were set according to the rules of the agrimonetary system. Features included the green rate freeze which protected farmers' incomes from the effects of sterling strength during 1997 and 1998. Agrimonetary compensation was paid in 1997 and 1998 to beef producers who received Suckler Cow Premium.

20 A new agrimonetary system was introduced to take account of the introduction of the euro on 1 January 1999. As a result, agrimonetary compensation payments have been paid to recipients of subsidies to ease the transition into the new agrimonetary system. This compensation, known as Transitional Agrimonetary Compensation (TAC) is being paid in three reducing annual instalments (or tranches) to recipients of Sheep Annual Premium in 1998, and to recipients of Beef Special Premium, Suckler Cow Premium, Extensification Payments and AAPS in 1999.

21 In addition, as a result of the strength of sterling against the euro, further agrimonetary compensation is being paid to UK producers. The 2000 package is known as Definitive Agrimonetary Compensation (DAC). It is being paid in two reducing instalments (or tranches) to recipients of Sheep Annual Premium in 1999 and to recipients of Beef Special Premium, Suckler Cow Premium and Extensification Payments in 2000. Recipients of AAPS in 2000 have received the first instalment of DAC (out of a possible three instalments).

22 There are two components of the 2001 package for beef producers, one in support of market prices and the other in support of premium payments. Recipients of Sheep Annual Premium also received agrimonetary compensation in 2001.

23 In both 2000 and 2001 agrimonetary compensation was paid to dairy farmers who were actively producing milk on the basis of the amount of milk quota held at 31 March in each year.

Accruals principle **24** Support payments are shown in the accounts in the year in which they became due to be paid. Normally this is the year in which the farmer carries out the production to which the subsidy relates. For agrimonetary compensation the payment becomes due only when the farmer has carried out the production and the government has decided to make the payment. A notable exception to this rule is the allocation of TAC. This is allocated to the years in which it was intended to offset reduced income. For beef and arable crops it covers 1999 to 2002, whereas for sheep it covers 1998 to 2001 (the Sheep Annual Premium being a deficiency payment based on market prices in the preceding year).

Accruals principle **25** Capital grants and transfers appear in the capital account as opposed to the income
Capital grants and account because they are not related to the activity of production. In 2001
transfers compensation for foot and mouth dominates (see also chapter 6, paragraph 5, and
(Table 8.5) table 6.4).

Agri-environment **26** Table 8.6 shows the expenditure on agri-environment schemes by country. Further
schemes details can be found in chapter 10 and areas of land within the various agri-
(Table 8.6) environment schemes are shown in table 10.2.

Agri-environment scheme payments

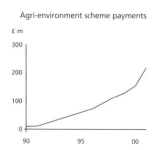

TABLE 8.1 Subsidies and levies included in the aggregate agricultural account

Enquiries: Jim Holding on 01904 455080   email: jim.holding@defra.gsi.gov.uk

£ million	Average of 1990-92	1997	1998	1999	2000	2001 (provisional)
Subsidies and levies on product (a)						
Crop subsidies						
Arable area payments on:						
wheat	..	493	466	420	458	349
barley	..	316	277	259	244	259
other cereal crops (b)	..	28	27	25	29	28
oilseed rape	..	167	155	175	110	103
linseed	..	37	48	102	29	10
peas and beans - stockfeed and human consumption	..	70	73	69	59	68
other crops	..	3	6	6	3	8
Other crop subsidies (c)	63	19	16	14	11	4
Livestock subsidies:						
Beef Special Premium (d)	44	271	256	273	216	242
Beef Marketing Payment Scheme	..	..	..	..	..	..
Suckler Cow Premium (d)	86	374	292	255	191	211
Slaughter Premium	..	..	..	..	43	84
Extensification Payment Scheme	..	..	..	..	122	126
Calf Processing Aid Scheme	..	54	52	20	..	..
Over Thirty Month Scheme	..	362	239	266	260	157
Hill Livestock Compensatory Allowance - cattle	62	55	85	87	55	..
Beef National Envelope (e)	..	..	..	..	13	26
Sheep Annual Premium	315	300	395	346	276	182
Hill Livestock Compensatory Allowance - sheep	80	54	84	86	54	..
FMD light lambs (f)	..	..	..	..	..	5
Other livestock subsidies (g)	110	..	..	..	..	..
Other subsidies. .						
Dairy agrimonetary compensation	..	..	..	..	22	79
Levies (h)						
milk superlevy	4	14	32	9	15	..
other levies prior to 1993 (i)	118	..	..	..	..	..
Total subsidies (less levies) on products	638	2 588	2 436	2 396	2 180	1 943
Other subsidies and levies (j)						
Set-aside (k)	..	90	88	170	127	184
Other animal disease compensation (l)	6	15	24	28	41	29
Less favoured areas support schemes (m) (n)	..	..	..	..	..	164
Agri-environment schemes:	17	92	114	131	156	220
Countryside Stewardship (o)	..	16	20	24	30	49
Countryside Premium (Scotland)	..	1	3	7	5	9
Tir Cymen & Tir Gofal	..	5	6	6	8	13
Organic Farming (p)	..	1	1	3	19	35
Environmentally Sensitive Areas	10	43	57	59	63	71
Nitrate Sensitive Areas	1	5	5	6	4	3
Woodland Schemes	1	8	9	10	12	14
SSSI (q)	2	12	12	14	13	16
other (r)	..	2	3	3	2	11
Taxes including vehicle licences	54	85	89	91	92	83
Other (s)	..	-	-	..	..	..
Total other subsidies less levies	- 31	113	138	238	232	514
Total subsidies less levies	607	2 700	2 574	2 633	2 411	2 457

source: DEFRA Statistics website, www.defra.gov.uk/esg

TABLE 8.1 *cont.*

(a) Contributes to basic prices and are included in output in table 6.1.

(b) Oats, rye, mixed corn and triticale.

(c) CAP hops and herbage seeds support, hemp and flax aid, oilseed rape and linseed support and British Potato Council compensation payments.

(d) Includes extensification premium and Northern Ireland deseasonalisation premium.

(e) In 2001 payments in England, Wales and Scotland were made to those claiming Suckler Cow Premium. In Northern Ireland payments were divided between those claiming Slaughter Premium or Suckler Cow Premium.

(f) A 'light lambs' disposal scheme, part of the Livestock Welfare Disposal Scheme. This scheme was introduced to cover lambs that could not be marketed as a result of the ban on exports and restrictions on movement of sheep arising from the outbreak of foot and mouth disease in 2001, and would have otherwise faced welfare problems.

(g) Beef and sheep variable premiums, hill cow, beef cow, calf, hill sheep, pig and calf subsidies.

(h) Excludes levies paid to non-governmental organisations. These are included in the aggregate accounts (table 6.1) under 'other miscellaneous expenditure'.

(i) Wheat, barley, oats, rye, mixed corn and milk co-responsibility levies.

(j) Not included in output but contribute to net value added at factor cost in table 6.1.

(k) Arable Area Payment and former 5 and 1 year Schemes.

(l) Tuberculosis, brucellosis, salmonella, Chernobyl, Newcastle and Aujeszky's disease, swine fever and avian influenza compensation and EIC egg scheme.In 2001 payments in England, Wales and Scotland were made to those claiming Suckler Cow Premium. In Northern Ireland payments were divided between those claiming Slaughter Premium or Suckler Cow Premium.

(m) Land area based schemes which replaced the Hill Livestock Compensatory Allowance Scheme in 2001. These are Tir Mynydd in Wales, Less Favoured Area Compensatory Allowances Scheme in Northern Ireland, Less Favoured Areas Support Scheme in Scotland and Hill Farm Allowance in England.

(n) The figures in tables 8.1 and 8.2 do not tally because table 8.2 contains revised figures for Northern Ireland .

(o) Also includes Arable Stewardship.

(p) Includes Organic Aid and Organic Farming schemes.

(q) Payments for land management for Sites of Special Scientific Interest administered by English Nature, Scottish Natural Heritage and Countryside Council for Wales.

(r) Includes Moorland, Habitat and Countryside Access Farming schemes.

(s) Guidance premium for beef and sheepmeat production, Pilot Beef and Sheep Extensification Scheme and farm accounts grant. Also includes historic data for fertiliser and lime grant and payments to small scale cereal producers.

TABLE 8.2 Subsidies and levies by country

Enquiries: Jim Holding on 01904 455080 email: jim.holding@defra.gsi.gov.uk

£ million   *Calendar years*

	England 2001	Wales 2001	Scotland 2001	Northern Ireland 2001
Subsidies on product (a)				
Crop subsidies				
Arable area payments on:				
wheat	330.3	1.9	16.2	0.8
barley	179.8	4.6	67.9	6.5
other cereal crops (b)	21.8	0.7	4.7	0.5
oilseed rape	94.0	0.4	9.0	-
linseed	9.8	0.1	0.4	-
peas and beans - stockfeed and human consumption	66.9	0.4	1.0	..
other crops	6.6	1.3	0.2	-
Other crop subsidies (c)	3.3	..	0.4	..
Livestock subsidies:				
Beef Special Premium (d)	126.1	23.8	46.3	45.7
Beef Marketing Payment Scheme	..	..	..	..
Suckler Cow Premium (d)	80.4	24.6	61.0	44.9
Slaughter Premium	48.9	7.4	12.7	15.3
Extensification Payment Scheme	49.7	15.0	33.7	27.4
Calf Processing Aid Scheme	..	..	..	..
Over Thirty Month Scheme	90.6	17.0	23.3	26.4
Hill Livestock Compensatory Allowance - cattle	..	..	..	..
Beef National Envelope (e)	10.6	3.0	7.6	5.2
Sheep Annual Premium	73.7	53.2	42.0	12.9
Hill Livestock Compensatory Allowance - sheep	..	..	..	..
FMD light lambs (f)	1.4	2.0	1.9	..
Other subsidies				
Dairy agrimonetary compensation	55.6	8.0	6.5	8.9
Total subsidies on products	1 249.5	163.3	334.8	194.5
Other subsidies (g)				
Set-aside (h)	162.0	1.4	19.8	0.6
Other animal disease compensation (i)	10.8	1.4	0.3	16.4
Less favoured areas support schemes (j) (k)	42.3	42.3	61.0	24.6
Agri-environment schemes:	144.5	34.3	33.9	7.0
Countryside Stewardship (l)	48.8	..	..	..
Countryside Premium (Scotland)	..	..	9.0	..
Tir Cymen & Tir Gofal	..	13.2	..	..
Organic Farming (m)	26.6	3.3	5.1	0.3
Environmentally Sensitive Areas	48.3	7.1	10.4	5.2
Nitrate Sensitive Areas	2.6	..	..	..
Woodland Schemes	7.5	0.3	4.8	1.5
SSSI (n)	8.5	2.4	4.6	..
other (o)	2.2	8.0	0.4	0.1
Total other subsidies	359.7	79.4	115.0	48.6
Total subsidies	1 609.1	242.7	449.8	243.1

source: DEFRA Statistics website, www.defra.gov.uk/esg

TABLE 8.2 *cont.*

(a) Contributes to basic prices and are included in output in table 6.1.

(b) Oats, rye, mixed corn and triticale.

(c) CAP hops and herbage seeds support, hemp and flax aid, oilseed rape and linseed support and British Potato Council compensation payments.

(d) Includes extensification premium and Northern Ireland deseasonalisation premium.

(e) In 2001 payments in England, Wales and Scotland were made to those claiming Suckler Cow Premium. In Northern Ireland payments were divided between those claiming Slaughter Premium or Suckler Cow Premium.

(f) A 'light lambs' disposal scheme, part of the Livestock Welfare Disposal Scheme. This scheme was introduced to cover lambs that could not be marketed, and would otherwise have faced welfare problems, as a result of restrictions on the movement of sheep arising from the outbreak of foot and mouth disease in 2001 and the ban on exports.

(g) Not included in output but contribute to net value added at factor cost in table 6.1.

(h) Arable Area Payment and former 5 and 1 year Schemes.

(i) Tuberculosis, brucellosis, salmonella, Chernobyl, Newcastle and Aujeszky's disease, swine fever and avian influenza compensation and EIC egg scheme.

(j) Land area based schemes which replaced the Hill Livestock Compensatory Allowance Scheme in 2001. These are Tir Mynydd in Wales, Less Favoured Area Compensatory Allowances Scheme in Northern Ireland, Less Favoured Areas Support Scheme in Scotland and Hill Farm Allowance in England.

(k) The figures in tables 8.1 and 8.2 do not tally because table 8.2 contains revised figures for Northern Ireland .

(l) Also includes Arable Stewardship.

(m) Includes Organic Aid and Organic Farming schemes.

(n) Payments for land management for Sites of Special Scientific Interest administered by English Nature, Scottish Natural Heritage and Countryside Council for Wales.

(o) Includes Moorland, Habitat and Countryside Access Farming schemes.

Table 8.3 Arable Area Payments Scheme (AAPS) and agrimonetary compensation

Enquiries: Ann Reed on 01904 455059 email ann.reed@defra.gsi.gov.uk

£ million

Calendar Year

	1999	2000	2001 (provisional)
Wheat	**419.7**	**458.4**	**349.1**
AAPS	361.3	424.5	339.4
Agrimonetary compensation	58.5	33.9	9.8
Barley	**259.4**	**244.3**	**258.9**
AAPS	223.3	224.7	252.8
Agrimonetary compensation	36.1	19.7	6.0
Oats	**20.3**	**23.4**	**23.3**
AAPS	17.5	21.7	22.8
Agrimonetary compensation	2.8	1.7	0.5
Other cereals	**5.2**	**5.5**	**4.4**
AAPS	4.5	5.1	4.2
Agrimonetary compensation	0.7	0.4	0.1
Oilseed Rape	**174.9**	**109.6**	**103.5**
AAPS	150.6	98.2	99.4
Agrimonetary compensation	24.4	11.5	4.1
Linseed	**101.9**	**29.4**	**10.2**
AAPS	87.7	23.9	7.8
Agrimonetary compensation	14.2	5.5	2.4
Peas & beans (a)	**68.7**	**59.2**	**68.4**
AAPS	59.1	54.2	66.8
Agrimonetary compensation	9.6	5.0	1.6
Other crops (b)	**5.5**	**2.7**	**8.1**
AAPS	4.8	2.4	7.7
Agrimonetary compensation	0.8	0.3	0.4
Set aside	**170.0**	**127.3**	**183.8**
AAPS	146.3	115.5	179.9
Agrimonetary compensation	23.7	11.8	4.0
Total	**1 225.7**	**1 059.9**	**1 009.6**
AAPS	1 055.0	970.1	980.8
Agrimonetary compensation	170.7	89.8	28.8

source: DEFRA Statistics website, www.defra.gov.uk/esg

(a) Includes total pea crop eligible for AAPS (80% assumed for stockfeed and 20% harvested dry for human consumption).

(b) 2001 figures include valuations for flax and hemp crops.

Table 8.4 Livestock subsidies and agrimonetary compensation

Enquiries: Keith Seabridge on keith.seabridge@defra.gsi.gov.uk. Tel: 01904 455091

£ million   Calendar Year

	1997	1998	1999	2000	2001 (provisional)
Beef Special Premium Scheme (a) (c)	**270.5**	**256.3**	**273.2**	**215.8**	**241.9**
Beef Special Premium	270.5	256.3	242.3	197.7	214.7
Agrimonetary compensation	..	..	31.0	18.1	27.2
Suckler Cow Premium Scheme (b) (c)	**373.6**	**291.9**	**255.0**	**191.1**	**210.8**
Suckler cow premium	302.3	244.6	225.8	173.2	187.9
Agrimonetary compensation	71.2	47.2	29.2	17.9	22.9
Sheep Annual Premium Scheme	**299.7**	**394.9**	**346.4**	**275.6**	**181.8**
Sheep annual premium	287.3	363.0	313.7	255.7	176.9
Agrimonetary compensation	12.4	32.0	32.6	19.8	4.9
Extensification Payment Scheme	..	..	..	**121.7**	**125.7**
Extensification payment	..	..	..	117.1	113.5
Agrimonetary compensation	..	..	..	4.6	12.2
Dairy agrimonetary compensation	..	..	..	**22.0**	**79.0**

source: DEFRA Statistics website, www.defra.gov.uk/esg

(a) Includes Northern Ireland Deseasonalisation Premium and TAC paid to 1999 recipient of the premium.

(b) Includes £50m BSE Support Payment in 1997, an EU funded package to support the beef industry during the BSE crisis.

(c) Includes extensification payments to 1999 and TAC paid to 1999 recipients, prior to extensification payments becoming a scheme in its own right in 2000.

Table 8.5 Capital payments

Enquiries: Keith Seabridge on keith.seabridge@defra.gsi.gov.uk. Tel: 01904 455091

£ million   Calendar Year

	1995	1996	1997	1998	1999	2000	2001 (provisional)
BSE - animal disease (from 1988)	11.1	7.0	4.6	19.9	10.4	3.1	13.8
BSE - selective cull (from 1997)	..	..	78.1	42.7	2.3	-	-
Scrapie (from 1998)	..	..	..	11.4	5.3	-	10.0
Pig welfare disposal scheme	..	..	..	..	..	8.7	3.9
Pig industry restructuring scheme	..	..	..	..	..	..	37.4
Foot and mouth disease (a)	..	..	..	..	..	..	1 274.1
Non-marketing of milk (1980 - 1986)	..	..	..	..	..	..	..
Milk outgoers (1984 - 1994)		..	..	..	..	..	..
Milk quota cuts (1987 - 1997)	26.0	26.1	26.9	..	..	..	..
Capital grants (b)	13.6	10.1	8.2	8.7	7.0	7.2	6.4

source: DEFRA Statistics website, www.defra.gov.uk/esg

(a) For full breakdown see table 6.4.

(b) Includes farm diversity, farm & conservation, agriculture improvement scheme, agriculture & horticulture and farm structures grants.

Table 8.6 Agri-environment scheme payments by country

Enquiries: Barbara Norton on 01904 455089   email: barbara.norton@defra.gsi.gov.uk

Expenditure (£ million)

Scheme year	1992	1993	1994	1995	1996	1997	1998	1999	2000	2001 (provisional)
Total expenditure	26.5	37.6	47.5	60.8	73.0	91.7	114.4	130.5	156.0	220.2
England										
Environmentally Sensitive Areas	10.4	16.2	19.3	24.3	26.8	28.6	37.6	39.5	40.9	48.3
Countryside Stewardship	5.3	8.5	10.5	11.6	10.9	15.7	19.9	23.4	28.9	47.3
Aable stewardship	..	..	..	..	..	..	..	0.5	0.9	1.5
Organic Conversion	..	..	..	0.1	0.3	0.7	1.2	2.3	15.4	26.6
Nitrate Sensitive Areas	1.3	1.4	1.6	3.6	4.1	4.7	4.7	6.2	3.9	2.6
Countryside Access	..	..	..	0.1	0.1	0.1	0.1	0.1	-	-
Habitat	..	..	..	1.0	1.4	1.8	1.8	1.9	1.9	2.0
Moorland	..	..	..	..	0.1	0.2	0.2	0.2	0.2	0.1
Woodland Schemes	1.5	2.2	2.9	3.4	3.8	4.7	5.4	5.9	6.0	7.5
English heritage, SSSI	7.5	7.6	6.6	6.6	6.1	6.3	6.2	7.8	7.6	8.5
Wales										
Environmentally Sensitive Areas	..	..	..	1.5	2.4	3.3	5.4	6.2	6.7	7.1
Tir Cymen	..	..	2.9	3.4	4.9	5.2	5.5	5.7	5.5	4.4
Tir Gofal	..	..	..	..	..	..	..	..	2.2	8.9
Organic Conversion	..	..	..	..	..	..	..	..	..	3.3
Habitat	..	..	..	..	..	..	..	..	..	7.3
Moorland	..	..	..	..	..	..	..	..	..	0.6
Woodland Schemes	..	..	..	0.1	0.2	0.2	0.2	0.2	0.3	0.3
Countryside council for Wales, SSSI	..	..	1.8	1.9	2.6	2.5	3.0	2.7	2.3	2.4
Scotland										
Environmentally Sensitive Areas	..	..	..	..	..	5.2	7.5	7.1	9.5	10.4
Countryside Premium	..	..	..	..	..	0.8	2.8	6.6	4.6	9.0
Organic Conversion	..	..	..	..	..	0.1	0.2	0.4	2.9	5.1
Habitat & moorland shemes	..	..	..	..	..	0.1	0.5	0.4	0.3	0.4
Woodland Schemes	..	1.0	1.2	2.1	2.4	2.8	3.3	3.8	4.3	4.8
Scottish natural heritage, SSSI	..	..	..	..	2.9	3.1	2.8	3.3	3.6	4.6
Northern Ireland										
Environmentally Sensitive Areas	0.5	0.6	0.6	1.1	4.0	5.6	6.1	6.2	6.0	5.2
Organic Conversion	..	..	..	..	..	..	..	..	0.4	0.3
Woodland Schemes	0.1	0.1	0.1	0.1	0.1	0.1	0.1	0.1	1.5	1.5
Other	..	..	..	..	..	..	..	..	0.2	0.1

source: DEFRA Statistics website, www.defra.gov.uk/esg

Chapter **9** Public expenditure on agriculture

Introduction 1 Table 9.1 shows public expenditure under the CAP and on national grants and subsidies, while Table 9.2 provides more detailed information on the costs of market regulation under the CAP. The tables exclude other expenditure that may benefit farmers (such as expenditure on animal health or on research, advice and education). They do, however, include some expenditure that benefits consumer and trade interests rather than producers directly. The figures for the financial years up to and including 2000/01 represent actual expenditure recorded in the Appropriation Accounts. The figures for 2001/02 are the latest estimates of expenditure.

Chart 9.1 Public expenditure under CAP by the Intervention Board (Rural Payments Agency from 16 October 2001) and Agricultural Departments

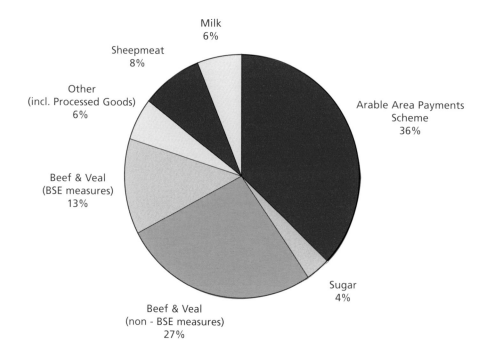

Milk
6%

Sheepmeat
8%

Other
(incl. Processed Goods)
6%

Beef & Veal
(BSE measures)
13%

Arable Area Payments
Scheme
36%

Sugar
4%

Beef & Veal
(non - BSE measures)
27%

Public expenditure 2 The Rural Payments Agency (RPA) was established on 16 October 2001 as a single
(Tables 9.1 and 9.2) accredited EU paying agency and an Executive Agency of DEFRA. It is the paying agency responsible for the EU Common Agricultural Policy (CAP) schemes in England and for certain schemes throughout the UK. The Scottish Executive, the National Assembly for Wales and the Department of Agriculture and Rural Development retain administration responsibilities for schemes within Scotland, Wales and Northern Ireland respectively. The RPA is also the recognised Funding Body responsible for receiving and accounting for all CAP Guarantee Funds. DEFRA retains overall responsibility for all policy matters relating to CAP. Table 9.1 indicates where payment responsibility has moved to the RPA from DEFRA.

3 Total UK expenditure in 2001/02 is forecast to increase by some £2.2 billion to £5.3 billion compared with expenditure the previous year. Spending in the UK under the CAP is forecast to increase from £2.7 billion in 2000/2001 to £2.9 billion in 2001/02. Chart 9.1 illustrates the expenditure breakdown by commodity sector, with more detail in Table 9.2.

4 The overall increase shown in table 9.1 is mainly attributable to the impact of the foot and mouth disease outbreak and in particular the cost of creating the Livestock Welfare Disposal Scheme (LWDS). The foot and mouth disease outbreak has impacted on the Over Thirty Months Scheme (OTMS). The foot and mouth restrictions had an inevitable impact on the number of OTMS presentations; however, as the outbreak subsided, the number of OTMS presentations caught up and expenditure is expected to reach similar levels to those of last year. The forecast for 2001/02 also reflects the commencement of BSE surveillance measures. This relates to the sampling of brain stems taken from over thirty-month casualties, fallen stock and a selection of OTMS animals presented at abattoirs. Expenditure in the cereals sector is forecast to decrease significantly. This is mainly due to a sharp reduction in the level of intervention buying and reduced expenditure on export refunds. The refund rates for the major grains have been set at zero throughout 2001/02. A significant increase in payments on the Suckler Cow Premium Scheme is also forecast for 2001/02. This is mainly accounted for by increased expenditure on extensification and new expenditure under the Beef National Envelope. Expenditure in the milk sector is also forecast to increase during 2001/02. This is mainly due to new expenditure on dairy agrimonetary compensation and much reduced levels of sales out of intervention. There has also been a significant reduction in the level of milk product exports due to the impact of foot and mouth disease, skimmed milk powder export refund rates being reduced to zero and an overall reduction in milk export refund rates.

5 Expenditure on other schemes in the UK is estimated to be £2.4 billion in 2001/02 compared with £324 million in 2000/01. This expenditure includes grants for conservation, exchequer funding of accompanying measures, assistance for agriculture in special areas and foot and mouth disease compensation and related disposal costs. However, it should be noted that payments under the English RDP are now administered by the RPA. The very large increase in forecast expenditure is mainly attributable to the cost of compensating farmers affected by the foot and mouth disease outbreak.

Intervention stocks

(Table 9.3) **6** Table 9.3 shows the level of opening and closing stocks and purchases into, and sales out of, intervention in the years 1997/98 to 2001/02.

TABLE 9.1 Public expenditure under the CAP and on national grants and subsidies

Enquiries: Rural Payments Agency on 0118 953 1725   email: Ian.Thomas@rpa.gsi.gov.uk

£ million   April/March (financial years)

	1997/98	1998/99	1999/00	2000/01	2001/02 (forecast)	2001/02 of which RPA administered)
II Market regulation and other agricultural support measures under the CAP						
A Expenditure funded via the Intervention Board (RPA 2001-02)						
(i) Expenditure by the Intervention Board (RPA 2001-02) (a):						
Cereals	34.6	156.4	54.0	20.7	12.2	12.2
Oilseeds	-	-	-	-	-	-
Sugar	111.2	161.8	125.4	118.0	106.0	106.0
Beef and veal (non-BSE)	0.7	2.0	0.8	3.6	1.4	1.4
Beef and veal (BSE)	849.0	446.6	331.9	358.3	366.0	366.0
Sheepmeat	-	0.7	2.0	0.8	- 0.4	- 0.4
Pigmeat	0.5	2.4	3.8	15.6	4.5	4.5
Milk products	207.6	156.6	108.4	87.8	172.1	172.1
Processed goods	36.4	41.0	38.4	29.3	27.3	27.3
Other (b)	41.1	45.1	45.7	30.8	21.3	21.3
Sub-total	1 281.1	1 012.6	710.4	664.9	710.4	710.4
(ii) Expenditure by Agriculture and other Departments (RPA 2001-02):						
Agricultural measures:						
Suckler Cow Premium Scheme	284.3	339.5	215.6	289.2	400.9	156.7
Beef Special Premium Scheme	197.9	294.0	213.6	275.9	274.5	142.3
Beef Deseasonalisation Scheme (NI)	6.0	5.6	2.6			
Slaughter Premium Scheme	..	..	..	23.1	80.8	56.0
Sheep Annual Premium	277.8	347.0	376.2	281.8	239.9	93.2
Payments to producers giving up some milk production	..	0.2	0.6	0.0	0.0	0.0
Arable Area Payments Scheme - cereals	855.0	777.8	611.4	690.7	645.5	539.6
- oilseeds	168.2	156.4	146.2	101.5	102.1	92.9
- linseed	49.4	46.9	86.9	24.2	7.9	7.6
- protein	58.3	72.4	58.5	54.9	68.5	66.8
- set-aside	90.8	87.3	144.1	118.8	186.9	165.0
Agrimonetary compensation	..	..	152.4	76.6	28.6	25.0
Definitive agrimonetary aid	-	-	-	18.5	0.0	0.0
Orchard Grubbing Scheme	..	0.8	-	-	-	-
UK National Honey Programme	..	0.5	0.3	0.3	0.2	0.1
School milk (Northern Ireland)	0.5	0.4	0.5	0.4	0.4	-
Hill Livestock Compensatory Allowances:						
- cattle (e)	..	..	14.4	5.9	-	-
- sheep (e)	..	..	15.5	15.4	-	-
BSE emergency measures	9.9	1.4	0.2	-	-	-
Sub-total	1 998.1	2 130.2	2 039.0	1 977.2	2 036.2	1 345.2
Rural development, Agri-environment and other measures:						
Environmentally Sensitive Areas	21.4	24.5	27.9	29.3	31.2	19.5
Nitrate Sensitive Areas	1.7	1.6	1.9	0.9	0.7	0.7
Pilot Beef and Sheep Extensification Scheme	..	..	..	..	..	..
Organic Farming	0.4	0.7	8.2	8.4	5.9	1.7
Countryside Stewardship	2.3	5.2	6.7	8.2	10.4	10.4
Tir Cymen	1.3	1.5	1.5	1.8	-	-
Tir Gofal	..	..	..	..	2.2	-
Moorland Scheme	0.2	0.1	0.2	0.2	0.1	0.1
Habitat Scheme	1.3	1.4	1.6	1.6	1.4	0.9

continued

TABLE 9.1 *cont.*

£ million   April/March (financial years)

	1997/98	1998/99	1999/00	2000/01	2001/02 (forecast)	2001/02 of which RPA administered)
Countryside Premium Scheme	..	0.6	1.2	1.7	3.0	-
Farm woodlands and forestry	12.7	14.7	17.4	17.1	16.2	2.5
Hill Farm Allowances	-	-	-	7.5	30.7	7.7
Arable Stewardship	-	-	-	-	-	-
Training	-	-	-	-	0.7	0.7
Processing and marketing grant scheme	-	-	-	-	1.5	1.5
Rural enterprise scheme	-	-	-	-	2.4	2.4
Other (unspecified saving)	..	..	..	..	..	-
Sub-total	41.3	50.3	66.6	76.8	106.4	48.1
Total	3 320.5	3 193.1	2 816.0	2 718.9	2 853.0	2 103.7
B UK expenditure by Agriculture and other Departments (RPA 2001-02)						
Environmentally Sensitive Areas	27.1	30.5	41.4	43.0	42.1	26.2
Nitrate Sensitive Areas	3.0	3.2	4.3	2.7	1.8	1.8
Pilot Beef and Sheep Extensification Scheme	..	..	..	..	..	-
Organic Farming	0.4	0.7	10.6	10.5	22.3	7.1
Processing and Marketing Grant Scheme	-	-	-	-	1.5	1.5
Countryside Stewardship	13.3	14.8	24.3	38.3	38.8	34.0
Tir Cymen	5.6	5.5	5.7	5.5	4.4	-
Tir Gofal	-	-	-	7.4	4.4	-
Vocational Training Scheme	-	-	-	-	0.7	0.7
Moorland Scheme	0.2	0.2	0.2	-	-	-
Habitat Scheme	1.2	1.3	1.5	1.6	1.4	-
Rural Enterprise Scheme	-	-	-	-	2.4	2.4
Countryside Premium Scheme	..	3.8	4.8	-	-	-
Hill Farm Allowances	-	-	-	-	33.2	33.2
Countryside Access/Set-aside Access Schemes	..	..	0.1	-	-	-
Farm woodlands and forestry	40.3	45.0	46.0	46.3	45.1	5.0
Energy Crops establishment grants	-	-	-	-	0.1	0.1
Optional Set-aside (5 and 1 year Schemes) (c)	0.1	..	..	..	..	-
Total	91.2	105.0	138.9	155.3	198.2	112.0
TOTAL (A+B)	3 411.7	3 298.1	2 954.9	2 874.2	3 051.2	2 215.7
II Price guarantees (national)						
Potatoes and assistance to egg industry	..	..	..	..	..	-
Wool	..	..	..	..	..	-
Total	..	..	..	..	..	-
III Support for conservation and other improvements						
Farm Diversification :						
capital grants	..	..	..	..	..	-
marketing and feasibility grants	..	..	1.0	1.9	1.6	-
Farm and Conservation Grant Scheme (EC) (d)	2.9	1.5	1.2	0.7	0.7	-
Agricultural Improvement Scheme (EC) (d)	..	..	..	..	..	-
Agricultural and Horticulture Development Scheme (d) (e)		..	..	..	..	..
Farm structures	..	..	0.1	0.1	-	-
Agriculture Improvement Scheme (national) (d)	..	..	..	..	..	-
NIADP, NIADOP and SPARD (d) (f)	15.1	4.8	2.4	..	..	-
Public access to ESAs	-	..	..	..	..	-
Rural Development Programme	3.2	6.4	8.4	22.2	14.5	-
Farm and Conservation Grant Scheme (National) (d)	0.8	0.6	0.1	0.3	0.2	-
Guidance Premiums	..	..	..	..	..	-
Farm accounts	..	..	..	..	..	-
ABDS	..	..	..	..	2.3	-
FBDS	..	..	..	..	2.3	-
Others (g)	..	..	..	..	..	--
Total	22.0	13.3	13.2	25.2	21.6	-

2001 (margin)

TABLE 9.1 *cont.*

£ million   April/March (financial years)

	1997/98	1998/99	1999/00	2000/01	2001/02 (forecast)	2001/02 of which RPA administered)
IV Support for agriculture in special areas						
Hill livestock compensatory allowances :						
- cattle (e)	90.7	70.3	86.6	13.2	42.9	-
- sheep (e)	43.8	86.9	89.8	27.3	24.3	-
LFACAS	..	..	..	20.1	17.4	-
LFA Support Scheme	..	..	..	42.6	52.6	-
Additional benefit under AHDS, NIADP and NIADOP, AHGS, AIS (EC), AIS (Nat), FCGS (EC), FCGS (Nat)	1.1	1.7	0.4	0.4	1.9	-
Others (h)	9.8	10.1	15.2	9.9	12.2	-
Total	145.4	169.0	192.0	113.5	151.3	-
V Other payments						
Foot and Mouth Disease compensation payments	-	-	-	28.8	1 047.0	..
Costs related to Livestock Welfare Disposal Schemes	..	..	..	..	451.0	451.0
Foot and Mouth Disease cleansing, disinfection and disposal costs (h)	..	..	..	0.3	530.3	27.5
Milk Outgoers Scheme (d)	..	..	..	..	..	..
Storm damage 1987	..	..	..	..	..	..
Sheep Compensation Scheme 1986 (d)	0.8	0.7	0.6	0.6	0.7	..
Cooperation grants	..	..	..	..	..	-
Crofting building grants and loans (net) (h)	3.0	0.6	0.7	0.2	1.5	..
Others (i)	0.1	..	..	..	..	-
Total	3.9	1.3	1.3	29.6	2 030.5	478.5
Total I to V (j)	3 583	3 482	3 161	3 042	5 255	2 694

source: RPA and DEFRA

(a) The figures are net of receipts treated as negative expenditure. Receipts from levies on the production and storage of sugar and isoglucose and on third country exports, which are regarded as Community Own Resources, are excluded.

(b) Includes eggs, poultrymeat, fruit and vegetables, hops, herbage seeds, dried fodder, peas and beans (to 1993/94), fisheries and flax. Also includes expenditure on products covered by the CAP but not produced to any significant extent in the United Kingdom (olive oil, rice, wine, grape must and hemp).

(c) Special arrangements apply for the EC funding of these schemes which is 60% for the 5-year scheme and 100% for the 1-year scheme (paid in 1992/93). The EC contribution towards the total expenditure shown is included in the figures at footnote (j).

(d) Farmers in special areas are also eligible for additional assistance. The estimated benefit is shown separately in section IV of the table.

(e) Includes the Farm and Horticulture Development Scheme.

(f) Except for the Northern Ireland Agricultural Development Programme (NIADP), the Northern Ireland Agricultural

Development Operational Programme (NIADOP), the Milk Outgoers, Woodland Grant and Sheep Compensation schemes expenditure from Northern Ireland block is excluded.

(g) Includes loan guarantees, grants for agricultural drainage in Scotland and farm structure loans.

(h) Excludes other foot and mouth disease costs not of direct benefit to the agricultural sector.

(i) Includes the Rural Enterprise programme, the Highlands and Islands Agricultural Programme, the Rural Development Programme, the Agricultural Development Programme for the Scottish Islands and grants for crofting.

(j) Includes producer organisations, forage groups and Shetland wool producers.

(k) Most expenditure under the CAP and some expenditure on other schemes is reimbursed by the EU. EU receipts, set out in the table below, do not always relate to expenditure in the year in which they are received. CAP expenditure is normally reimbursed two months in arrears.

Reimbursement of spending on structural measures (Section III) is normally a year in arrears.

	1995/96	1996/97	1997/98	1998/99	1999/00	2000/01	2001/02 (forecast)
£ million	2 674	3 304	3 466	3 343	2 563	2 682	2 392

TABLE 9.2 Public expenditure under the CAP by the Intervention Board, Rural Payments Agency (2001-02) and other Departments - major commodities

Enquiries: Rural Payments Agency on 0118 953 1725   email: Ian.Thomas@rpa.gsi.gov.uk

£ million   April/March (financial years)

	1997/98	1998/99	1999/00	2000/01	2001/02 (forecast)
Cereals					
Intervention purchases/sales	4.0	89.4	- 18.8	- 19.2	2.6
Intervention storage costs	4.1	17.7	17.8	10.1	1.3
Export refunds	23.7	45.6	46.5	25.0	6.1
Internal market measures	2.8	3.7	8.4	4.8	2.2
Total cereals	34.6	156.4	53.9	20.7	12.2
Oilseeds					
Export refunds	..	..	..	..	..
Internal market measures	..	..	..	..	..
Total oilseeds	..	..	..	..	..
Sugar					
Export refunds	61.4	112.6	84.9	73.9	67.5
Internal market measures	49.8	49.2	40.5	44.1	38.5
Total sugar	111.2	161.8	125.4	118.0	106.0
Beef and veal (non-BSE)					
Intervention purchases/sales	..	..	..	- 1.5	-
Intervention storage costs	..	..	..	1.4	- 0.1
Internal market measures	0.7	2.0	0.8	1.6	1.3
Export refunds	..	..	..	-	0.2
Suckler Cow Premium	284.3	339.5	215.6	289.2	400.8
Special Premium	197.9	294.0	213.6	275.9	274.5
Deseasonalisation Premium	6.0	5.6	2.6	-	-
Slaughter Premium Scheme	-	-	-	25.2	80.8
Hill Livestock Compensatory Allowances:					
- cattle	..	..	14.4	-	-
- sheep	..	..	15.6	-	-
Other measures	..	..	..	5.8	-
Total beef and veal (non-BSE)	488.9	641.1	462.6	597.6	757.5
Beef and veal (BSE)					
Intervention purchases/sales	130.4	- 29.3	- 84.9	-	-
Intervention storage costs	52.8	24.2	12.3	-	-
Export refunds	- 1.7	- 1.9	0.0	-	-
Over Thirty Month Scheme purchases	287.9	263.8	264.6	239.8	232.8
OTMS slaughter, disposal costs etc.	196.0	116.2	128.7	117.8	117.1
Surveillance work	..	..	..	..	15.5
Clean beef top up	-	-	-	-	-
Calf Processing Aid Scheme	53.3	51.0	10.0	-	-
Beef Stocks Transfer Scheme	4.5	-	-	-	-
Beef and Beef Products (disposal service)	1.5	-	-	-	-
Animal Feed Disposal Service	0.4	-	-	-	-
Selective cull	114.8	18.9	1.2	0.7	0.7
Suckler Cow Compensation	6.9	-	-	-	-
Special Premium Compensation	- 6.6	-	-	-	-
Beef Marketing Payment Scheme	0.1	-	-	-	-
Veal Marketing Payment Scheme	-	-	-	-	-
Meat & Livestock Commission promotion	2.5	-	-	-	-
Other measures	16.2	5.2	0.2	0.1	-
Total beef and veal (BSE)	859.0	448.1	332.1	358.4	366.1

TABLE 9.2 *cont.*

£ million

April/March (financial years)

	1997/98	1998/99	1999/00	2000/01	2001/02 (forecast)
Sheepmeat					
Internal market measures	277.8	347.7	378.2	298.1	239.5
Pigmeat					
Internal market measures	-	-	0.6	0.1	0.3
Export refunds	0.5	2.4	3.2	1.9	0.4
Pig Welfare (Disposal) Scheme	-	-	-	13.6	3.8
Total pigmeat	0.5	2.4	3.8	15.6	4.5
Milk products					
Intervention purchases/sales	21.8	41.4	- 20.4	- 34.4	1.3
Intervention storage costs	1.2	1.9	2.5	1.5	1.2
Export refunds	132.3	87.4	79.6	63.4	41.0
Internal market measures	67.5	58.4	56.3	50.7	49.0
Co-responsibility/Supplementary Levy	- 15.1	- 32.0	- 9.1	- 15.0	- 0.2
Payments to those giving up milk production (a)	0.4	0.1	0.6	2.5	1.8
Agrimonetary Compensation	..	..	..	22.0	78.4
Total milk products	208.1	157.2	109.5	90.7	172.5
Processed goods					
Export refunds	36.0	39.8	37.7	29.3	27.3
Arable area payments scheme					
Internal market measures	1 221.7	1 140.8	1 199.5	1 082.4	1 039.5
Rural Development Measures					
Hill Farm Allowance Scheme	-	-	-	7.5	30.7
Environmentally Sensitive Areas	-	-	-	29.2	31.2
Nitrate Sensitive Areas	-	-	-	0.9	0.7
Organic Farming Scheme	-	-	-	8.4	5.9
Farm Woodland Schemes	-	-	-	17.0	5.6
Countryside Stewardship Schemes	-	-	-	8.2	10.4
Training	..	..	..	0.1	0.7
Processing and Marketing Grant Scheme	..	..	..	..	1.5
Rural Enterprise scheme	..	..	..	..	2.4
Sub total	-	-	-	71.3	89.1
Others					
Export refunds	7.8	19.6	18.2	6.5	0.5
Internal market measures	77.6	84.2	98.6	31.6	40.0
Miscellaneous	- 2.7	- 6.0	- 3.5	- 1.4	- 1.7
Total others	82.7	97.8	113.3	36.7	38.8
TOTAL	3 320.5	3 193.1	2 816.0	2 718.7	2852.9

source: RPA

(a) Some paid by the Intervention Board from 1994/95.

AHDS - Agriculture & Horticulture Development Scheme

AHGS - Agriculture & Horticulture Grant Scheme

AIS (EC) - Agricultural Improvement Scheme (EC)

AIS (Nat) - Agricultural Improvement Scheme (National)

FCGS (EC) - Farm & Conservation Grants Scheme (EC)

FCGS (Nat) - Farm & Conservation Grants Scheme (National)

ABDS - Agricultural Business Development Scheme

FBDS - Farm Business Development Scheme

LFACAS - Less Favoured Area Cattle and Sheep

CCDS - Crofting Community Development Scheme

SPARD - Sub-Programme for Agriculture and Rural Development

TABLE 9.3 Commodity intervention in the United Kingdom

Enquiries: Rural Payments Agency on 0118 953 1725   email: Ian.Thomas@rpa.gsi.gov.uk

Thousand tonnes

Commodity	1997/98			1998/99			1999/00			2000/01			2001/02			
	Closing/ opening stock (a)	Pur-chases	Sales	Closing/ opening stock (a)	Pur-chases	Sales	Closing/ opening stock (a)	Pur-chases	Sales	Closing/ opening stock (a)	Pur-chases	Sales	Closing/ opening stock (a)	Pur-chases	Sales	Closing stock (a)
Wheat: feed	-	-	-	-	-	-	-	-	-	-	-	-	-	-	-	-
bread	-	-	-	-	18	-	18	24	25	17	-	17	-	-	-	-
Barley	11	525	-	535	837	545	827	91	604	313	20	322	10	1	-	11
Rye	1	-	1	-	8	-	8	6	-	14	1	15	-	-	-	-
Beef: boneless	59	47	7	99	4	29	74	-	73	1	-	1	-	-	-	-
bone in	-	-	-	-	-	-	-	-	-	-	-	-	-	-	-	-
Butter	5	-	3	2	-	1	1	11	-	10	2	2	10	3	-	13
Skimmed milk powder	29	25	-	53	29	-	80	14	61	32	-	32	-	-	-	-

Source: RPA

(a) These figures may not always equate to (closing stock = opening stock + purchases - sales) because of end of year stock adjustments arising from unfulfilled sales contracts etc, and because each figure is rounded.

2001

Chapter 10 Environment

Introduction

1 Environmental accounts are compiled by the Office for National Statistics for the United Kingdom as a whole and are undergoing developments. They are "satellite accounts" to the main National Accounts. They provide information on the environmental impact of economic activity and on the importance of natural resources to the economy. Environmental accounts use similar concepts and classifications of industries to those employed in the National Accounts, and they reflect the recommended European Union and United Nations frameworks for developing such accounts. The statistics shown in this chapter are intended to fit in with this framework.

Farming and the environment

2 Some 75 per cent of the United Kingdom land area is managed by farmers and the countryside has historically been determined by agricultural management practices.

3 Farming has helped to create and maintain a wide range of ecosystems which shape our countryside - hedges, banks, field margins, woodlands, wetlands and ditches that provide refuge and sources of food for a wide range of plants and animals. Without farming much of our current rural landscape would be significantly different. And an extensively farmland landscape provides opportunities for public amenity and access. But the drive for improvement and efficiency since the 1940s has also led to the loss of some of those habitats and features. Agricultural changes - largely in response to changes in policy and markets - have, in particular, affected the biological diversity of our countryside through declines in and losses of important wildlife habitats such as hay meadows, wetlands, moorland, heathland and downland.

4 Water is an important resource and farming plays an important part in protecting it. As well as protecting the quality of both surface and groundwater supplies, farming maintains drainage systems and has an important role in flood prevention. The discharge of nutrients and pesticides can contaminate water both as a source for drinking water and for aquatic life. Emissions from animals, vehicles, equipment and soil cultivation can result in greenhouse gases contributing to global warming, but also to localised air pollution. However, plant growth is a short term sink for carbon dioxide and produces oxygen and 'fresh air'. Soil is an important resource. As well as improving and conserving soil, cultivation can expose soil to wind and water erosion.

5 The manufacture of fertiliser, pesticides and equipment uses finite resources, but farming is increasingly becoming more sustainable by contributing to renewable power (poultry litter and straw burning power stations), growing short rotational crops, producing biodiesel and by management of waste products.

Valuing the environment

6 In order to produce environmental accounts for agriculture, all the positive and negative impacts of agriculture on the environment need to be considered. This valuation is very subjective.

7 The cost of damage can be measured by the 'cost to return to the original state'. Restoration of hedges, walls and other features can be valued as the cost of restoration. Pollution of water could be valued as the cost of returning the water to drinking or river quality but the loss of soil from the land or loss of biodiversity in the water are more difficult to value.

8 In some cases the environment cannot be returned to the original state, such as the global effects of greenhouse gases or permanent loss of biodiversity. For example the use of fossil fuels releases carbon from sinks formed millions of years ago - this cannot be balanced with carbon utilised in plant growth where at the very most it is only tied up for tens or hundreds of years before being re-released. Likewise, the damage from emissions into the air is difficult to value as any effects may take a comparatively long time to come to light, though the emissions themselves could be quantified.

9 For many aspects such as the general look of the landscape and biodiversity one has to rely on 'willingness to pay' studies. These are based on how much respondents say that they would be willing to pay for specific environmental goods. These techniques are not generally accepted as providing definitive estimates but can provide the general scale of the value.

10 A study by Olivia Hartridge and David Pearce (Is UK Agriculture Sustainable? Environmentally Adjusted Economic Accounts for UK Agriculture, July 2001) showed that the provision of environmental services by agriculture is outweighed by damage caused by the release of greenhouse gases and water pollution. This is an active area of research and further developments on how to measure agriculture's impact on the environment are necessary to establish a framework and then to attach values to items within the framework before we can put reliable values into the accounts. We will be consulting with stakeholders on our development plans.

11 Agricultural methods maintain the countryside and produce two-thirds of our food; the growth of grass and crops provides oxygen whilst being a short term sink for carbon. As well as the beneficial and detrimental effects of agriculture the alternative uses of the land would need to be looked at for the full picture.

12 The environmental accounts for agriculture draw upon statistics compiled in "Towards Sustainable Agriculture: a pilot set of indicators", available on the DEFRA website. There are many gaps and omissions in the available data and for many aspects it has only been possible to describe the mechanisms without quoting statistics. The accounts are divided into the following sections covering:

- State of the environment – general indicators of biodiversity on farmland;

- Emissions – levels of damaging emissions to waterways and the atmosphere;

- Resource use – use of finite and renewable resources.

State of the environment
(Chart 10.1)

13 Bird populations are good indicators of the state of wildlife in the countryside since they have a wide habitat distribution and are near the top of the food chain. Therefore, they reflect changes in habitat diversity and in the food chain. Surveys of bird populations have been carried out since 1970 by the British Trust for Ornithology. This gives a continuous record of changes over 30 years.

Chart 10.1 Key bird populations

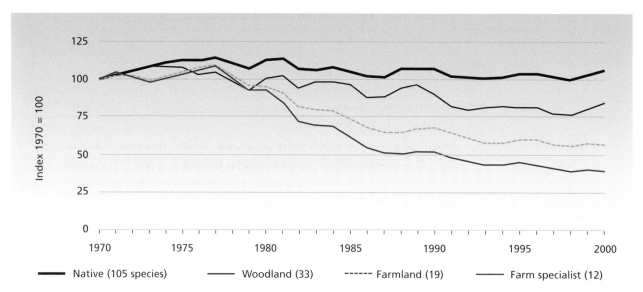

Source: DEFRA/RSPB/BTO Wild Bird Indicator - published in December 2001

Note: The number of species is reduced from the previous version due to the exclusion of species for which only range size during the two breeding bird atlas periods (1970 & 1990) is available.

14 Chart 10.1 shows that farmland bird populations declined by almost half between 1977 and 1993, but have been relatively stable since. Farmland species decreased by about 2 per cent in 2000 following the 3 per cent increase recorded for 1999 and are now slightly below the level in 1993. Within this category the subset of farm specialists has followed a similar pattern albeit with a larger fall. The woodland bird index declined by around 30 per cent between 1974 and 1998. Woodland birds have since increased by 5 per cent in 2000 and 4 per cent in 1999 rising to their highest level since 1990.

15 The reasons for the decline in farmland bird numbers are complex. Changes to the way farmland has been managed over the last 30 years have adversely affected birds by reducing food availability and nesting opportunities. In arable systems the key changes include loss of mixed farming, increased use of fertilisers and pesticides, and reduction in spring sowing of cereals. In grassland systems the key changes include increased mechanisation, increased use of fertilisers, drainage and loss of rough grassland, and the switch from hay to silage.

16 The UK Biodiversity Action Plan includes targets to reverse this decline; 26 species have been identified including the skylark, grey partridge, corn bunting, song thrush and bullfinch. Targets include reversing the decline in breeding and over-wintering numbers and also increasing their range and habitats. DEFRA is using the farmland bird population index as a biodiversity indicator for sustainable agriculture. The index also forms the basis for DEFRA's Public Service Agreement target to reverse the long-term decline in farmland birds by 2020.

Emissions **17** Emissions from the agriculture industry include losses of fertiliser and pesticides to water, greenhouse gases from animals, manure and slurry to the atmosphere, as well as emissions from direct and indirect energy consumption. It is difficult to collate data on actual emissions as they come from diffuse and hugely variable biological sources resulting in insufficient data being available. For fertiliser and pesticide losses, data are based on samples of river and ground water and so do not give a full or continuous picture of losses. Nor do they show whether they will break down rapidly or persist in the environment. Over 50 per cent of UK nitrous oxide emissions come from manure and slurry. The recent fall in emissions is largely due to the reduction in inorganic nitrogen fertiliser use and falling numbers of cattle.

18 Integrated Farm Management (IFM) is a whole-farm policy providing the basis for efficient and profitable production which is economically viable and environmentally responsible. IFM integrates beneficial biological processes into modern farming practices using advanced technology. It aims to minimise environmental risks while conserving, enhancing and recreating environmentally important features. This involves the consideration in agricultural organisation and planning of: soil management and crop nutrition; crop protection; pollution control and waste management; energy efficiency; landscape and wildlife features and animal husbandry. Agriculture Departments use demonstration farms and supply advice on management practice including the use of manure. Farmers in Nitrate Vulnerable Zones (NVZs) can apply for farm waste and slurry grants; since 1996 £330,000 has been paid through the scheme. Linking Environment and Farming (LEAF) actively promotes IFM with a self-assessment audit and over 1,300 members now consider IFM in their management decisions involving over 140,000 hectares.

19 The DEFRA Codes of Good Practice for the Protection of Soil, Air and Water provide a benchmark of good practice with advice on avoiding pollution. Provisional results from the 2001 Farm Practices Survey in England indicate that 66 per cent of farmers responding to the survey had at least one of the codes (these are available free from DEFRA publications and are on the DEFRA website), whilst 49 per cent had copies of all three. Ownership rates were highest amongst the largest farms; for example, two thirds of the largest sheep farms had all three codes of practice. There is also a code of practice for the safe use of pesticides which was owned by 60 per cent of English farmers responding to the survey, including nearly 90 per cent of farmers of the largest arable and horticultural holdings. In Scotland a composite code exists – the Prevention of Environmental Pollution from Agricultural Activities (PEPFAA). An evaluation of the PEPFAA code was carried out by the Central Research Unit of the Scottish Executive in 1999. This study showed that over 50 per cent of farmers had heard of the code and that around 30 per cent considered they owned or had access to a copy of the code. These codes are available free from the Scottish Executive.

Resource Use **20** Resources can be renewable (sustainable), or non-renewable (using up finite
(Table 10.1) resources). Some finite resources are consumed by the agricultural industry and are used in the form of petroleum, coal & gas and in production of electricity. They are also used in the form of metals in the manufacture of equipment and in the

chemicals in fertilisers and pesticides. Other resources important to agriculture include soil and water. Soil is the basis for plant growth and its careful management is essential for all farming so that it remains a renewable resource. Water is also renewable so long as over-extraction does not have a permanent effect on the level of the water table particularly during times of drought or when polluted with agricultural waste. Carbon from the atmosphere is taken up by all plant growth acting as a short-term carbon sink.

21 The data available on consumption of finite resources is limited to statistics on direct and indirect energy consumption. Table 10.1 shows estimated direct and indirect use converted in to PetaJoules (Joules x 1015) for purposes of comparison. This is the energy consumed in agricultural production and not in the manufacture and distribution of food.

22 Energy used by the agricultural industry represented two-thirds of one per cent of overall UK energy consumption in the year 2000. Compared with the previous year energy use by the agricultural industry was reduced. This went against the overall UK energy supply trend which increased.

23 Energy use in agriculture can be classified into:

- direct use of energy (including electricity) for heating and motive power;

- indirect input in the form of manufactured goods, fertilisers, pesticides and machinery.

24 The direct energy data is provided on 'as supplied to agriculture' basis. Energy supplied basis does not include the efficiency of generation and losses in handling and refining.

25 The use of direct energy by agriculture has declined slowly in the last 15 years. During this period the use of electricity has declined slowly with the reduction of housed livestock. The development of new and enhanced sustainable farming technologies, such as minimum tillage, should help the sector further to improve its energy efficiency.

26 The energy supplied to agriculture declined significantly between 1999 and 2000. The amount of energy used by agriculture in any year, however, will depend to some extent on factors that are outside the sector's control - most notably the weather.

27 The most dominant indirect input of energy arises from the use of fertilisers. The more rational use of fertiliser has been reflected in a steady decline in energy use with a 20 per cent reduction over 15 years. Similarly, energy supplied in the form of pesticides has reduced by 23 per cent over the same period as a result of more efficient use and greater environmental responsibility. The adoption of organic production methods gives further scope for the reduction of indirect energy use from both fertilisers and pesticides. These gains may be offset to some extent by the greater direct inputs in the form of additional field operations or cover materials for the control of weeds and pests.

2001

28 Agricultural tractor purchase is affected year on year by economic factors. Table 10.1 shows the energy required in their manufacture and maintenance. The trend is for fewer units of higher horsepower to be purchased. Larger machines give benefits both in direct and indirect energy use through greater efficiency of field operations. In 2000 the horsepower of the average new tractor registered was 119.6 hp, a 32 percent increase since 1990.

29 The fuel for a fifth of the electricity used by agriculture can be derived from agricultural biomass. Renewable fuels include livestock wastes and straw to which are now added energy biomass crops. Agricultural biomass is the source of 15 per cent of renewable energy in the UK.

30 Conversion technologies are aimed at two levels:

- Small scale on-farm combustion for heat production. The table shows the level of direct use of biomass by agriculture;

- Electricity generation for sale under the Non-fossil Fuel and the (forthcoming) Renewables Obligations.

31 Biofuels produced by agriculture will contribute to the policy of the generation of 10 per cent of national electricity by 2010 from renewable resources. In England the Rural Development Programme provides a scheme for planting biomass crops (Short Rotation Coppice and the grass Miscanthus) and establishing producer groups. DEFRA is working with the Department of Trade and Industry to encourage the further development of renewable energy.

32 Renewable-energy power station developments in the UK since 1992 include the world's first four poultry litter power stations, the world's largest straw-fired power station and the first gasifier power station fuelled by short rotation coppice. These have a combined generating capacity of 118 MWe (MegaWatts electrical). In addition, there are smaller stations operating on wood fuel. The permissions are in place for a 36 MWe straw and energy crop fuelled power station project.

Agri-environment schemes
Tables 8.6 & 10.2

33 Agri-environment schemes generally make payments for the management of land to: improve and extend wildlife habitats; conserve historic, geological and landscape features and to restore traditional aspects of the countryside. They aim to make conservation part of management practice. Expenditure on these and other rural development schemes will increase further through the Rural Development Programme by modulation (see chapter 8). The funding for these schemes comes jointly from the EU and the UK government (see Chapter 9).

34 Table 8.6 shows expenditure on individual agri-environment schemes by country. The figures for organic farming schemes are for conversion programmes. A single scheme year has been used as the individual schemes use different years. The data for each scheme is in the year in which the bulk of that scheme's payments are made. Further information on the specific schemes can be found on the DEFRA, SEERAD, NAWAD and DARD websites.

35 The areas of land within these schemes continue to increase. Table 10.2 shows the cumulative areas of land within individual schemes by country. Altogether some 1.3

million hectares are farmed under Scottish agri-environment schemes; data is not available for Countryside Premium Scheme. It is being replaced by the Rural Stewardship scheme and the first payments are due in 2002. In Northern Ireland nearly 800,000 hectares will be coming under their countryside management scheme; the initial payments are due in 2002.

36 Some 623,202 hectares of land is registered (June 2001) as being farmed organically in the UK. Emphasis is placed on maintaining healthy soil, and measures such as adequate rotations have to be taken to ensure its fertility and biological activity. Inputs into organic production are strictly regulated and the use of artificial fertilisers and pesticides is excluded. Conversion to organic farming systems provides gains in terms of soil health and fertility. Biodiversity benefits from the use of crop rotations, as well as the absence of synthetic pesticides, herbicides and fertilisers.

37 Sites of Special Scientific Interest (SSSIs) schemes are administered by English Nature, Scottish Natural Heritage and Countryside Council for Wales with payments to farmers to protect and conserve, for example, the landscape, rare species, and biodiversity.

TABLE 10.1 Direct and indirect energy consumption

Enquiries: Barbara Norton on 01904 455089   email: barbara.norton@defra.gsi.gov.uk

units: PJ, Joules x 10^{15}	1985	1990	1993	1995	1997	1999	2000
Fuel							
Direct energy - total	59.3	56.3	57.1	58.1	56.8	51.9	46.5
Coal	0.3	0.5	0.3	0.4	0.2	0.1	0.1
Biomass	..	3.1	3.1	3.1	3.1	3.1	3.1
Natural gas	2.9	4.0	4.7	4.5	5.7	5.9	5.3
Electricity	14.4	13.9	13.8	14.2	13.7	13.8	13.6
Petroleum	41.7	34.8	35.2	35.9	34.1	29.0	24.4
Indirect Inputs							
Indirect Energy total	181.0	172.6	150.0	164.5	160.0	150.1	145.1
Fertiliser	133.8	128.8	104.6	115.8	113.8	109.7	107.5
Pesticide	10.6	10.1	10.3	9.8	10.3	9.5	8.2
Tractor purchases	15.0	11.4	12.8	14.6	12.3	9.5	9.3
Animal Feeds	21.6	22.2	22.2	24.2	23.6	21.4	20.2
Total Energy	240.3	228.9	207.1	222.6	216.8	202.0	191.6

Source : ADAS, Reports prepared for DEFRA using : Digest of UK Energy Statistics, Agriculture in the UK, Fertiliser Manufacturers Association, Agricultural Engineers Association, Crop Protection Association

Table 10.2 Environment schemes - land in schemes by country

Enquiries: Barbara Norton on 01904 455089   email: barbara.norton@defra.gsi.gov.uk

Thousand hectares

Scheme year	1992	1993	1994	1995	1996	1997	1998	1999	2000	2001 Provisional
England										
Environmentally Sensitive Areas	129.4	266.5	346.4	424.5	433.6	469.1	501.2	523.5	531.9	577.0
Countryside Stewardship	..	..	..	..	90.9	105.5	118.3	139.9	192.1	263.3
Arable Stewardship	..	..	..	..	..	..	..	1.8	2.0	2.0
Organic Conversion	..	..	1.6	2.1	4.7	6.1	10.7	16.1	95.9	134.5
Nitrate Sensitive Areas	5.4	9.2	9.2	12.9	19.6	23.4	24.4	27.8	15.6	9.5
Countryside Access	..	..	..	0.1	0.1	0.1	0.1	0.1	0.1	0.1
Habitat	..	..	3.7	5.1	6.7	6.8	6.0	7.0	7.1	7.1
Moorland	..	..	..	6.5	11.3	15.3	15.8	15.8	15.8	15.8
Woodland Schemes	12.8	16.3	18.6	21.0	22.5	25.4	29.3	32.7	36.2	37.7
English Heritage, SSSI										
Wales										
Environmentally Sensitive Areas	..	..	15.4	24.3	33.4	54.2	62.0	67.2	70.7	..
Tir Cymen	..	..	..	..	..	..	..	..	88.6	..
Tir Gofal	..	..	..	..	..	..	..	52.0	50.0	..
Organic Conversion	..	..	..	..	..	..	..	..	34.2	..
Habitat	..	..	..	..	..	..	..	..	7.3	
Moorland	..	..	..	..	..	..	..	..	0.6	
Woodland Schemes	..	..	0.2	0.5	0.5	0.5	0.7	0.9	0.7	..
Countryside Council for Wales, SSSI	..	..	37.2	46.0	46.6	50.3	52.3	55.4	62.6	..
Scotland										
Environmentally Sensitive Areas	120.6	124.0	149.6	300.8	374.1	441.1	515.3	639.5	771.7	771.1
Countryside Premium	..	..	..	..	..	..	..	..	..	..
Organic Conversion	..	..	..	0.1	16.5	19.1	23.2	75.8	212.3	232.7
Habitat & Moorland shemes	..	..	..	..	0.1	0.2	0.5	0.6	1.6	3.8
Woodland Schemes	..	..	..	..	..	..	..	..	..	..
Scottish Natural Heritage, SSSI	..	..	..	..	..	..	..	..	..	..
Northern Ireland										
Environmentally Sensitive Areas	..	..	..	82.9	117.9	131.3	144.8	151.7	154.3	..
Organic Conversion	..	..	..	..	..	..	0.5	1.0	1.0	3.8
Woodland Schemes	..	..	..	..	..	..	..	..	..	..
Other	..	..	..	..	..	..	..	..	..	..

source: DEFRA Statistics

GLOSSARY

Definitions of terms used in the aggregate agricultural account.

Term	Table 6.1 ref.	Definition
Agricultural Industry		All activities taking place within businesses that carry out any agricultural activities. These businesses include all farms and specialist agricultural contractors.
Capital formation in livestock	7	Production of animals that will be used as the means of production, e.g. breeding animals.
Other agricultural activities	8	Agricultural activities that do not result in sales of final product, e.g. quota leasing, contract work.
Inseparable non-agricultural activities	9	Non-agricultural activities which are included within the business level accounts and are inseparable, e.g. some cases of bed & breakfast and recreation facilities.
Gross output at basic prices	10	Output including directly paid subsidies that are closely correlated with production of a specific product. The output of the agricultural industry includes some non-agricultural activities and transactions within the industry.
Basic prices		Market price plus directly paid subsidies that are closely correlated with production of a specific product.
Subsidies (less taxes) on product	11	Subsidies and taxes on products are shown in detail in table 6.7; all subsidies are recorded on an as due basis.
Intermediate consumption	20 (13:18)	Consumption of goods and services, e.g. feed, seeds, fertiliser, pesticides.
Gross value added (at basic prices)	21 (10-20)	Gross Output at basic prices less Intermediate Consumption.
Consumption of fixed capital	22	The reduction in value (at current prices) of capital assets used in the production process, e.g. buildings, plant, machinery, vehicles and livestock.
Net value added at basic prices	23 (21-22)	Gross Value Added at basic prices less Consumption of fixed capital.
Other Subsidies (less taxes) on production	24	Subsidies and taxes not closely correlated with production of a specific product, e.g. agri-environment payments, set-aside, animal disease compensation.
Net value added at factor cost	25 (23+24)	Net Value Added at basic prices plus other subsidies (less taxes) on production
Compensation of employees	26	The full costs of employees to the business including national insurance contributions.
Total Income From Farming (TIFF)	29	Income to those with an entrepreneurial interest in the agricultural industry, e.g. farmers, partners, spouses and most other family workers.

Further information

Additional information is available at:

DEFRA	www.defra.gov.uk
National Assembly for Wales	www.wales.gov.uk
Scottish Executive	www.scotland.gov.uk
Department Of Agriculture And Rural Development (Northern Ireland)	www.dardni.gov.uk
Food Standards Agency	www.food.gov.uk
Rural Payments Agency (formerly the Intervention Board and Regional Service Centres)	www.rpa.gov.uk/
England Rural Development Programme (ERDP)	www.defra.gov.uk/erdp
Countryside Agency	www.countryside.gov.uk
English Nature	www.english-nature.org.uk
Countryside Council for Wales	www.ccw.gov.uk
Scottish Natural Heritage	www.snh.org.uk
Environment Agency	www.environment-agency.gov.uk
British Potato Council	www.potato.org.uk
Home-Grown Cereals Authority	www.hgca.co.uk
Meat and Livestock Commission	www.mlc.org.uk
Livestock and Meat Commission for Northern Ireland	www.lmcni.com
Forestry Commission	www.forestry.gov.uk
Scottish Agricultural College	www.sac.ac.uk
Valuation Office Agency (GB)	www.voa.gov.uk
Valuation and Land Agency (NI)	vla.nics.gov.uk
Agriculture Development Advisory Service	www.adas.co.uk
Office for National Statistics	www.statistics.gov.uk
HM Customs and Excise	www.hmce.gov.uk
European Union (Eurostat)	www.europa.eu.int

If you find the information in *'Agriculture in the United Kingdom'* useful, you should be aware of these publications:

Agricultural Census Statistics in the UK (formerly the Digest)

Agricultural Census Statistics in the UK brings together the main results of the Annual Agricultural and Horticultural Censuses which are held each June in England, Scotland, Wales and Northern Ireland.

Agricultural Atlas

The *Agricultural Atlas* contains colour maps showing the distribution of main census items in England by 5km grid square.

June Census Analyses

A wide variety of detailed data covering England at county and regional level. Includes frequency distribution tables for main census items.

Historical Agricultural Data

Historical trend analyses covering the last 20 years are available at county level for livestock in England. During 2002 similar data for crops will also be published in this format.

All the above are available on the World Wide Web at **www.defra.gov.uk** under 'Economics and Statistics', or for further information please call the Farming Statistics Team on 01904 455332.

Farm Incomes in the United Kingdom 2000/01

'Farm Incomes in the United Kingdom 2000/01' provides an authoritative and detailed source of information on the incomes and financial structure of the agricultural industry in each of the four countries of the United Kingdom.

The seventeenth volume, in an annual series, gives detailed analyses of farm incomes (including some information on off-farm incomes), assets and liabilities and aggregate incomes for the agricultural industry for each of the four countries of the United Kingdom. Detailed farm accounts data, based on the Farm Business Survey (Farm Accounts Scheme in Scotland) are shown by farm type, business size and tenure. In addition, it contains estimates of the gross margins for a range of crop and livestock enterprises in England and Wales. In most tables the years covered are 2000 and 2001. The publication will only be available on the DEFRA Web site [at **www.defra.gov.uk/esg/pubs/pubs.htm**] in mid-March 2002. Other enquiries about this World Wide Web publication should be directed to:

> Mr Roger Price,
> Department for Environment, Food and Rural Affairs,
> Economics (Farm Business) Division,
> Whitehall Place West (Room 702),
> Whitehall,
> London
> SW1A 2HH
> Tel. 020 7270 8620

Other information is available, including an index showing published DEFRA Statistics and the dates on which they will be issued. This can be accessed on the World Wide Web at **www.defra.gov.uk/esg** and via 'faxback'. To access faxback, dial 0870 444 0200 for commodity statistics or 0870 444 0201 for farming statistics and follow the voice instructions. Although our statistics notices continue to be free, you will incur a charge of approximately 50p per minute for the telephone call. Typically, a single sided document will take about one minute to transmit, with any subsequent sheets about 45 seconds each.

AGRICULTURE IN THE UNITED KINGDOM 2001

Agriculture in the United Kingdom 2001 is the fourteenth in a series which succeeds the *Annual Review of Agriculture* White Paper. It provides, in an accessible format, information on the economic conditions of the United Kingdom agriculture industry. The Government will draw on this information when considering policy issues, including proposals by the European Commission for agricultural support in 2002/2003.